Glencoe

Algebra 1

Integration
Applications
Connections

D1290241

Answer Key Masters

GLENCOE
McGraw-Hill

New York, New York   Columbus, Ohio   Woodland Hills, California   Peoria, Illinois

Glencoe/McGraw-Hill

A Division of The **McGraw-Hill** *Companies*

Send all inquiries to:
Glencoe/McGraw-Hill
936 Eastwind Drive
Westerville, OH 43081-3374

ISBN: 0-02-824866-X

Algebra 1
Answer Key Masters

2 3 4 5 6 7 8 9 10 066 03 02 01 00 99 98

Contents

1. Multiply 15 times 20.

2. Yes; evaluate s^3 where s is the measure of a side.

3. x used as a factor 7 times

4. Algebraic expressions include variables.

5. Tonya; Sample explanation: The square of any number between 0 and 1 is less than the number; $0.5^2 = 0.25$ and $0.5 > 0.25$.

6. $a^4 \cdot b^2$

7. $3y^2 - 6$

8. 7 to the fifth power

9. 3 times x squared increased by 4

10. 4^3

11. a^7

12. 36

13. 32

14. πr^2

15. $k + 20$

16. $16p$

17. a^7

18. $49 + 2x$

19. $\frac{2x^2}{3}$ or $\frac{2}{3}x^2$

20. $5m + \frac{n}{2}$ or $5m + \frac{1}{2}n$

21. $b + 8$

22. $3w$

23. 4 times m to the fifth power

24. x squared divided by 2

25. c squared plus 23

26. one half the cube of n

27. 2 times 4 times 5 squared

28. 3 times x squared minus 2 times x

29. 8^2

30. 10^5

31. 4^7

32. t^3

33. z^5

34. d^{10}

35. 49

36. 81

37. 64

38. 125

39. 16

40. 243

41. $3(55 - w^3)$

42. $4(r + s) + 2(r - s)$

43. $a + b + \frac{a}{b}$

44. $4s$

45. $y + 10x$

46. 5^3; 125 cubes

47. 16; 16

48a. $7x$

47a. They are equal; no; no.

48b. $3x$

47b. no; for example, $2^3 \neq 3^2$

49a. $3.5x$

49b. $3.5y$

49c. $3.5x + 3.5y$

48c. $7x - 3x$

50. $2\ell w + 2\ell h + 2wh$

1–2 Patterns and Sequences
Pages 15–18

1. When the problem is difficult, you can solve simpler problems and look for a pattern that could help you solve the more difficult problem.

2. Sample answer: 7, 12, 17, 22

3. Either person could be right. You would need to know the fourth term to decide which pattern is correct.

4a. 52 pieces

4b. $y + 2$

5.

6. 49, 40

7. $5x + 1$, $6x + 1$

8a. 3 units; 4 units; 5 units; 6 units

8b. 7 units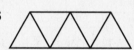

8c. 12 units

8d. $n + 2$ units

9a.

4^1	4^2	4^3	4^4	4^5
4	16	64	256	1024

9b. 6; $4^6 = 4096$

9c. 4; When the exponent is odd, 4 is in the ones place.

10.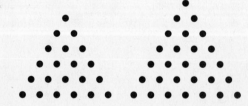

11.

12.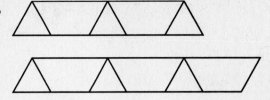

13. 48, 96

14. 10, 11.5

15. 25, 36

16. 10, 13

17. $a + 7$, $a + 9$

18. $x - 4y$, $x - 5y$

19a.

20a.

3^1	3^2	3^3	3^4	3^5	3^6
3	9	27	81	243	729

19b. White; even-numbered figures are white.

20b. 3, 9, 7, 1, 3, 9,...

20c. 7, 1, 3, 9, 7, 1

19c. 12 sides; The shapes come in pairs. Since $19 \div 2 = 9.5$, the 19th figure will be part of the 10th pair. The 10th pair will have $10 + 2$, or 12 sides.

20d. 1; 100 is divisible by 4. According to the pattern, all powers with exponents divisible by 4 have 1 in the ones place.

21a. 4; 9; 16; 25

22a. Replace y with 2 and find $2 \cdot 2$.

21b. The sums are perfect square numbers; that is $1^2, 2^2, 3^2, 4^2, 5^2, ...$

22b. 2, 4, 6, 8, 10, 12, 14, 16, 18, 20

21c. 10,000

21d. x^2

22c. even numbers

23a. i. 1,999,998; **ii.** 2,999,997; **iii.** 3,999,996; **iv.** 4,999,995

23b. 8,999,991

24a.

10^1	10^2	10^3	10^4	10^5
10	100	1000	10,000	100,000

24b. 1

25. 4, 7, 10, 13, 16

26. 13, 21, 34, 55, 89, 144

27. 1:13 p.m.

28a. 30 cans

28b. 328 cans

29a. 100 cards

30. $q^2 - 8$

29b–d. See students' work.

31. x cubed divided by 9

32. m^9

33. 4^3; 64 cubes

34. $20,000 + 24x$

35. $x + \frac{1}{11}x$

Algebra 1

1–3 Order of Operations
Pages 22–24

1. Multiply 7 and 2.

2. parentheses, brackets, braces, fraction bar; to show what operation should be completed first

3. First divide 30 by 6, which equals 5. Second, add 5 and 5, which equals 10. Third, square 10, which equals 100. Fourth, multiply 100 times 2, which equals 200.

4. 21

5. 173

6. 1

7. 4

8. 36

9. 25

10. Sample answer: $xz - \dfrac{w}{y}$

11. $a^2 - a$ is less.

12. 78 in²

13. 14

14. 63

15. 14

16. 26

17. 9

18. 0

19. 60

20. 51

21. $\dfrac{11}{18}$

22. 172

23. 6

24. 4.3

25. 126

26. 2

27. 147

28. 18

29. 126

30. $\dfrac{24}{125}$

31. $r^2 + 3s$; 19

32. $t(4s + r)$; 11

33. $(r + s)t^2$; $\dfrac{7}{4}$

34. $r^5 - t$; $31\dfrac{1}{2}$

35. 19.5 mm

36. 34 yd

37. 22 in.

38. 83

39. 16.62

40. 95.58

41. 3.77

42a.

x	$\frac{1}{2}$	1	10	50	100
$\frac{2x-1}{2x}$	0	$\frac{1}{2}$	$\frac{19}{20}$	$\frac{99}{100}$	$\frac{199}{200}$

43a. Sample answer:
   $(4 - 2)5 \div (3 + 2)$

43b. $4 \times 2 \times 5 \times 3 \times 2$

45a. $\frac{1}{3}Bh$

45b. 198,450 m³

47. 16, 19.5

49. June 18

51. $t + 3$

53. 9 more than two times y

42b. As the value of x gets larger, the value of the expression approaches 1.

42c. 1

44a. $30(3) + 25(4) + 65(3)$

44b. $385

46. 32, 64

48. $a^5b^4c^3d^2e$, $a^6b^5c^4d^3e^2f$

50. h^5

52. 121

1–4 Integration: Statistics   Stem-and-Leaf Plots
Pages 28–31

1. Answers will vary. Responses should include least and greatest values, frequency in categories, distribution, clusters, and gaps.

3. Step 1: Decide on stems.
   Step 2: Place stem and leaves on chart.
   Step 3: Arrange leaves in numerical order.

5. stem 12, leaf 2

7. stem 126, leaf 9

9a. 35 tickets sold one day

9b. 31 tickets

9c. 75 tickets

9d. 1043 tickets

2. not beginning an axis at 0, not using uniform spacing on scales, not indicating that the scale does not begin at 0 with a broken line

4. Sample answer: I can use stem-and-leaf plots to keep a record of my math test scores. From this plot, I can determine my lowest and highest scores. I can also determine the interval where most of my scores fall.

6. stem 6, leaf 3

8. 0, 1, 2, 3, 4, 5

10a.

Stem	Leaf
2	6 6 7 8 9 9
3	0 0 1 1 2 2 3 4 5 6
4	0 1 2 3
5	2 4 6 4|3 = 43

10b. 26 floors

10c. 56 floors

11. stem 13, leaf 3

13. stem 44, leaf 3

15. stem 111, leaf 3

17. stem 14, leaf 2

19. stem 111, leaf 4

21. rounded to the nearest hundred:
9, 12, 24, 27, 38, 39, 40

23a. Sample answer: Both teens and young adults had similar distribution of responses.

23b. Sample answer: The market research shows that the new game is equally appealing to teens and young adults. Therefore, we should concentrate our marketing efforts towards both teens and young adults.

25a.

1980	Stem	1993
4	1	3
6	2	4
8 5 1	3	3 7 7
	4	6
1	5	

$3|7 = 3700$

25b. 3000 to 3900; 3000 to 3900

25c. Sample answer: Farm sizes seem to be shrinking.

27. 15

29a. $\frac{s}{5}$

29b. 2 miles; yes

31.

10d. 9 buildings

10e. 6 buildings

12. stem 4, leaf 5

14. stem 9, leaf 9

16. stem 0, leaf 8

18. stem 1, leaf 0

20. 9, 11, 12, 13, 27, 39, 43, 44, 48, 50, 77

22. 8, 12, 13, 17, 27, 29, 33, 37

24a. 6.8

24b. 8.0

24c. 9 more

24d. 5.1

26a.

Stem	Leaf
3	0 0 1 1 1 4 5 6 6 8 9
4	2 2 3 3 4
5	0 1 3 4 4
6	1 5 6 9
7	2
8	0 0 7 8

$6|5 = 650$

26b. 580 miles

26c. 11 rivers

28. 29

30. $\frac{11}{64}, \frac{13}{128}$

1. An open sentence cannot be true or false until the variable or variables are replaced. If a sentence has no variables, the sentence is automatically either true or false.

2. An expression is two or more numbers and/or variables with operation symbols. Open sentences have numbers, variables, or expressions connected with a relationship symbol such as $=$, $<$, or $>$.

3. A solution set is a subset of the replacement set that makes the open sentence true.

4. Replace n with 10 and see if the statement is true. Then replace n with each of the other elements in the replacement set. Write a set of the elements from the replacement set that makes the open sentence true.

5. See students' work.

6. true

7. false

8. {1, 2}

9. {1, 3, 5}

10. 4

11. 75

12a. $g = 15{,}579 + 6220 + 18{,}995$

12b. 40,794 glasses

13. false

14. true

15. true

16. false

17. true

18. false

19. {5}

20. {10, 15, 20}

21. $\left\{\frac{1}{2}, \frac{3}{4}\right\}$

22. $\left\{\frac{3}{4}, 1, \frac{5}{4}\right\}$

23. {10, 15, 20}

24. $\left\{\frac{1}{2}, \frac{3}{4}, 1, \frac{5}{4}\right\}$

25. 3

26. 27

27. 2

28. $1\frac{3}{4}$

29. $4\frac{5}{6}$

30. 17

31. Sample answer: $p = 1$ and $q = 2$, $p = 2$ and $q = 10$, $p = 3$ and $q = 8$, $p = 4$ and $q = 20$, and $p = 5$ and $q = 15$.

32a. $t = 3(144)$; Texas should have about 3 times their yearly average.

32b. 432 tornadoes

Algebra 1

32c. Sample answer: Write an equation that estimates the number of tornadoes that Oklahoma will have in the next five years; $t = 5(45)$.

33a. $C = \dfrac{3500 \cdot 4}{14}$

33b. 1000 Calories

34a. $d = (3.36)(1.5)$

34b. 5.04 mi

34c. Yes; it can travel 100 ft in $100 \div 2.3$ or 43.5 s

35. 2, 5, 6, 7, 9

36. 85 goals

37. 8

38. $10a + 9$, $12a + 11$

39. 5 less than x to the fifth power

40. $a + b + c$

Self Test
Page 36

1. $3a + b^2$

2. $w^5 - 37$

3. 11:04, 11:08, 11:51, 11:55

4. 39

5. 408

6. 18

7.

Stem	Leaf
4	8
5	4
6	7
7	7
8	5 9

$6 \mid 7 = 67$

8.

Stem	Leaf
1	0
2	4 5
3	5 9
4	5
7	5 6

$3 \mid 5 = 350$

9. {6, 7, 8}

10. {4, 5}

1. two or more things that are exactly alike

2. No; because $a + 1 \neq a$.

3. You cannot divide by 0.

4. 1

5. Reverse the numerator and the denominator.

6. $\frac{1}{7}$

7. $\frac{2}{9}$

8. $\frac{1}{c}$

9. c

10. b

11. e

12. g

13. d

14. a

15. f

16. mulitiplicative inverse; multiplicative property of zero; additive identity; multiplicative identity

17. 9; substitution (=); substitution (=); multiplicative property of zero; multiplicative identity; additive identity

18. 2; substitution (=); substitution (=); multiplicative property of zero; additive identity; substitution (=)

19a. $4(20) + 7$

20. $\frac{1}{9}$

19b. $4(20) + 7$
$= 80 + 7$ substitution (=)
$= 87$ substitution (=)

19c. 87 years

21. 9

22. 4

23. $\frac{1}{p}$

24. $\frac{a}{2}$

25. $\frac{2}{3}$

26. symmetric (=)

27. substitution (=)

28. substitution (=)

29. multiplicative identity

30. multiplicative inverse

31. multiplicative inverse, multiplicative identity

32. additive identity

33. symmetric (=)

34. multiplicative property of zero

35. reflexive (=)

36. transitive (=)

37. substitution (=);
substitution (=);
multiplicative identity;
multiplicative inverse;
substitution (=)

38. substitution (=);
substitution (=);
multiplicative identity;
multiplicative property of zero;
substitution (=);
additive identity

39. substitution (=);
substitution (=);
substitution (=);
multiplicative identity

40. 4; substitution (=);
substitution (=);
multiplicative identity

41. 25; substitution (=);
substitution (=);
multiplicative identity

42. 51; substitution (=);
substitution (=);
substitution (=);
substitution (=)

43. 7; substitution (=);
substitution (=);
additive identity

44. 1; substitution (=);
substitution (=);
substitution (=);
substitution (=);
substitution (=);
multiplicative inverse

45. 126; substitution (=);
multiplicative inverse;
substitution(=)

46a. No; a number is never less than itself. Sample answer: 4 is *not* less than 4.

46b. No; if one number is less than a second number, then the second number can never be less that the first number. Sample example: 4 is less than 5, but 5 is *not* less than 4.

46c. Yes; if one number is less than a second number and a second number is less than a third number, then the first number will be less than the third number. Sample example: $4 < 5$ and $5 < 6$, so $4 < 6$.

47a. $[21(12 \cdot 2)] + [23(15 \cdot 2)] + [67(10 \cdot 2)]$

48a. $0.32 + 0.23(14)$

48b. 3.54; substitution (=);
substitution (=)

47b. 2534; substitution (=); substitution (=); substitution (=)

47c. $25.34

48c. $3.54

49. true

50. 3

51. false

52. when there are 2 sets of data

53. See students' work.

54. 16

55. 36

56. 13, 16

57. 12y

1–7 The Distributive Property
Pages 48–50

1. According to the distributive property, $2(a - 3) = 2a - 6$.

2. Sample answer: $5a + 3a + a + 2b$

3. Multiply 3 times $2x$ and 3 times 4. Subtract the product of 3 and 4 from the product of 3 and $2x$.

4.

	$x + 1$	
	x	1
4	x	1
	x	1
	x	1

5. b

6. e

7. a

8. d

9. c

10. $6x + 18$

11. $2a - 2b$

12. 1485

13. 60

14. 2.5

15. 7

16. $\frac{3}{5}$

17. $4y^4$, y^4

18. $3a^2$; $9a^2$; $4c$; c

19. $3t^2 + 4t$

20. in simplest form

21. $23a^2b + 3ab^2$

22. $6p + 1\frac{2}{3}q$

23. $5.35(24) + 5.35(32)$; $5.35(24 + 32)$

24. $8 + 2t$

25. $5g - 45$

26. $5x + 15$

27. $24m + 48$

28. $28y - 4$

29. $5a - ab$

30. 485

31. 52

32. 1632

33. 60

34. 5994

35. 645

36. $33x$

37. in simplest form

38. $10n + 12n^2$

39. $12a + 15b$

40. $21x^2y - 28xy^2 + 7xy$

41. in simplest form

42. $30a + 5b$

43. $3x + 4y$

44. $\frac{5}{3}c - \frac{1}{2} + cb$

45. $1\frac{3}{5}a$

46. $14g + 14$

47. $9x + 5y$

48a. yes; if $C \neq 0$

48b. Change the / in the If statement to $\wedge$; only for $C = 1$.

49. No; sample counterexample: $2 + (4 \cdot 5) \neq (2 + 4)(2 + 5)$

50a. $4(16.15 + 32.45)$; $4(16.15) + 4(32.45)$

50b. $194.40

51a. $2[x + (x + 14)] = 4x + 28$

52. symmetric (=)

51b. 96

51c. 527 ft²

53. multiplicative property of zero

54. {5, 6}

55a. $d = (1129)(2)$

56.

Stem	Leaf
2	9
3	6 6 7
4	5 5
5	1 5 8

$3|7 = 37$

55b. 2258 ft

57. 2

58. $25a^5, 30a^6$

59. 8 years

60. $2k - 37$

1. Answers will vary. Sample answer: $(2 \cdot 3) \cdot 5 = 2 \cdot (3 \cdot 5)$
$$6 \cdot 5 = 2 \cdot 15$$
$$30 = 30$$

2. Use the commutative property of multiplication to rewrite the problem as $5 \cdot 2 \cdot 6.5$. Since $5 \cdot 2 = 10$, the answer 65 can be determined without a calculator or paper and pencil.

3. The commutative properties allow a different *ordering* of numbers while the associative properties allow a different *grouping* of numbers.

4. Division is *not* commutative since the examples have different quotients.

5. See students' work.

6. associative $(+)$

7. commutative $(+)$

8. substitution $(=)$

9. associative $(\times)$

10a. distributive property

10b. commutative $(\times)$

10c. associative $(\times)$

10d. substitution $(=)$

11. $5a + 2b$

12. $5p + 10q$

13. $14x + 3y$

14. $2.9x + 1.2y$

15. $6z^2 + (7 + z^2 + 6)$
$= 6z^2 + (z^2 + 7 + 6)$
commutative $(+)$
$= (6z^2 + z^2) + (7 + 6)$
associative $(+)$
$= (6 + 1)z^2 + (7 + 6)$
distributive property
$= 7z^2 + 13$
substitution $(=)$

16. commutative $(+)$

17. multiplicative identity

18. distributive property

19. associative $(\times)$

20. multiplicative property of zero

21. distributive property

22. substitution $(=)$

23. commutative $(\times)$

24. associative $(+)$

25. associative $(+)$

26a. distributive property

26b. commutative $(+)$

26c. associative $(+)$

27. $10x + 5y$

28. $9a + 3b$

29. $7x + 10y$

30. $4 + 8ac + 12b$

31. $10x + 2y$

32. $5y^4 + 3y^2$

33. $32a^2 + 16$

34. $9.5x + 5.5y$

35. $5x$

36. $5.5x + 6$

37. $\frac{3}{4} + \frac{5}{3}m + \frac{4}{3}n$

38. $\frac{23}{10}p + \frac{6}{5}q$

39. $2(s + t) - s = 2s + 2t - s$
    distributive property
    $= 2t + 2s - s$
    commutative ($+$)
    $= 2t + (2s - s)$
    associative ($+$)
    $= 2t + (2s - 1s)$
    multiplicative identity
    $= 2t + (2 - 1)s$
    distributive property
    $= 2t + 1s$
    substitution ($=$)
    $= 2t + s$
    multiplicative identity

40. $\frac{1}{2}(p + 2q) + \frac{3}{4}q = \frac{1}{2}p + q + \frac{3}{4}q$
    distributive property
    $= \frac{1}{2}p + \left(q + \frac{3}{4}q\right)$
    associative ($+$)
    $= \frac{1}{2}p + \left(1q + \frac{3}{4}q\right)$
    multiplicative identity
    $= \frac{1}{2}p + \left(1 + \frac{3}{4}\right)q$
    distributive property
    $= \frac{1}{2}p + \frac{7}{4}q$
    substitution ($=$)

41. $5xy + 3xy = (5 + 3)xy$
    distributive property
    $= 8xy$
    substitution ($=$)

42. $4(a + b) + 2(a + 2b)$
    $= 4a + 4b + 2a + 4b$
    distributive property
    $= 4a + 2a + 4b + 4b$
    commutative ($+$)
    $= (4 + 2)a + (4 + 4)b$
    distributive property
    $= 6a + 8b$
    substitution ($=$)

43. $\frac{1}{100}$; Each denominator and the following numerator represent the number 1. The resulting expression is 1 in the numerator and 100 in the denominator multiplied by numerous 1s. Since 1 is the multiplicative identity, the product is $\frac{1}{100}$.

44. No; answers will vary. Sample answer: $5 - 3 \neq 3 - 5$.

45. No; Sample example: Let $a = 1$ and $b = 2$; then $1 \ast 2 = 1 + 2(2)$ or 5, and $2 \ast 1 = 2 + 2(1)$ or 4.

46a. no

46b. Sample answer: practicing piano and doing homework

46c. Sample answer: putting clothes into the washer and dryer

47a. $G = 3.73$

47b. See students' work.

48. $\frac{4}{5}$

49. $100d + 80d + 8d$, $188d$

50. substitution ($=$)

51. $\frac{3}{2}$

52. true

53.

Stem	Leaf
9	5 7 7 9 9 9
10	0 0 0 1 1 1 1 3

$10 | 3 = 103$

54. 7

55. ▼ ▲

56. $5p^6$

1–9 A Preview of Graphs and Functions
Pages 59–62

1. The numbers represent different values. The first number represents the number on the horizontal axis and the second represents the number on the vertical axis.

2. Sample answers: $3000; $800

3a. world population in billions of people from 1900 to the year 2000

3b. horizontal axis: time in years; vertical axis: population in billions

3c. Sample answer: (1925, 2): In 1925 the world's population was about 2 billion people. (1950, 2.5): In 1950 the world's population was about 2.5 billion people.

4. Sample answer: Every day, the patient's condition becomes worse.

3d. The estimated world population for the year 2000 is 6.2 billion.

3e. Sample answer: The world's population has increased since 1900.

5a. Graph 3

5b. Graph 4

5c. Graph 2

5d. Graph 1

7a. False; *A* is the younger player, but *B* runs the mile in less time.

7b. False; *A* made more 3-point shots, but *B* made more 2-point shots.

7c. True; *B* is the older player and *B* made more 2-point shots.

7d. True; *A* is the younger player and *A* made more free-throw shots.

9. Graph a; An average person makes no money as a child, then his or her income rises for several years, and finally levels off.

6.

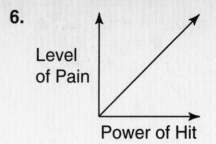

Level of Pain

Power of Hit

The independent variable is how hard you hit your thumb; the dependent variable is how much it hurts.

8. Graph b; The bus gains speed, and then travels at a level speed. Later, it slows to a stop. Then the pattern continues.

10a. Sample answer: Jorge saved steadily from January to June. In July, he withdrew money to go on vacation. He started saving again in September. Then in November he withdrew money for holiday presents.

10b. The domain includes the months of the year; the range is the amount of money.

11a. Graph 5

11b. Graph 3

11c. Graph 1

11d. Graph 4

11e. Graph 6

11 f. Graph 2

12.

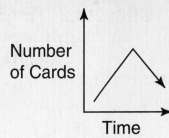

13.

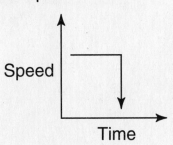

14.

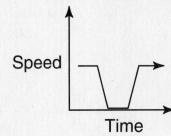

15.

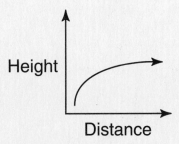

16. See students' work.

17a. independent variable: time in years; dependent variable: millions of dollars

17b. In 1991 the telethon raised 45 million dollars.

17c. Money raised in the telethon decreased, then increased steadily.

17d. The money raised increased.

17e. Answers will vary. See students' work.

18. Sample answer: Rock music was the best seller. Rap music sold better than country music.

19. $7p + 11q + 9$

20. $23a + 42$

21. 14

22. true

23. $\frac{1}{3}Bh$

1. An arrow would be drawn, starting at 0 and going to −4. Starting at −4, an arrow would be drawn to the right 6 units long. The arrow ends at the sum of 2.

2.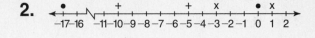

3.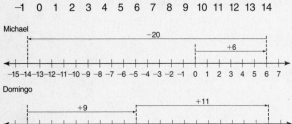

4. See students' work.

5.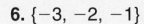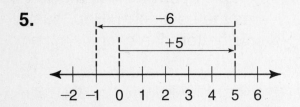

6. {−3, −2, −1}

7. {−1, 0, 1, 2, ...}

8.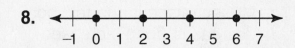

9.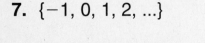

10.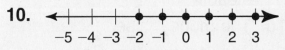

11. −4 + (−3) = −7

12. 4 + (−4) = 0

13. −5

14. −22

15. 9-yard gain

16. {..., −2, −1, 0, 1, 2, 3}

17. {−4, −3, −2, −1}

18. {0, 2, 5, 6, 8}

19. {−7, −3}

20. {−2, −1, 1, 2}

21. {...,−5, −4, −3, −2, −1, 0}

22.

23.

24.

25. ← • • • + + + + + →
-4 -3 -2 -1 0 1 2 3 4

26. ← + • • • • • • + + →
-2 -1 0 1 2 3 4 5 6

27. ← • • • + + + + + + →
-7 -6 -5 -4 -3 -2 -1 0 1

28. ← + + + + + + • • • →
-5 -4 -3 -2 -1 0 1 2 3

29. ← + • • • • • + + →
-7 -6 -5 -4 -3 -2 -1 0 1

30. ← + • • • • • • • + →
-11 -10 -9 -8 -7 -6 -5 -4 -3 -2

31. 13

32. −13

33. −5

34. −13

35. −12

36. 2

37. 6

38. 0

39. −23

40. See students' work.

41. $-17 + 82 = 65$; $65°F$

42a. 11 P.M. the same day

42b. 7 A.M. the same day

42c. 12 noon the same day

42d. 8:30 P.M. the same day

43a. 4°F

43b. −31°F

43c. −15°F

43d. 9°F

44. See students' work.

45.

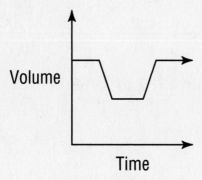

46. b

47. commutative (×)

48. $37a + 23b$

49. substitution (=)

50. $41 = x$

51. 13.9

52. 11, 12.5, 14

1. See students' work.

3. See students' work.

5. from 35 to 80

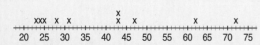

2. See students' work. Sample answer: Line plots give a depiction of information but the data may have a large range. Tables state all the possibilities but may not be organized numerically.

4. from 0 to 70

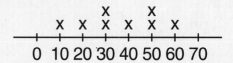

6a.

6b. $1950-$11,475

6c.

7a.

7b. 70 mph; cheetah

7c. 30 mph

7d. 30 mph

7e. 12

7f. 4

9a. from 20 to 75 by 5s

9b. yes, 25 and 42

8a. from 1787 to 1959

8b.

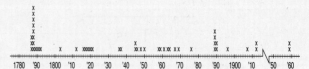

8c. Yes, 1788; states ratified constitution and became official United States of America.

10a.

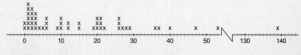

10b. yes; 1, 2, and 3

9c. See students' work.

9d. See students' work.

11a. Ms. Martinez's

11b. No; in Ms. Martinez's class, the hours that the students talked on the phone were close to each other (4 $\pm$ 2 hours). In Mr. Thomas' class, the students had a wider range of hours spent talking on the phone. The range was from 0 to 8 hours, with no hours clustered around a certain number.

13. Mr. Thomas', 3.6 hours; Ms. Martinez's, 3.7 hours; yes

15. associative ($\times$)

17. 2

10c. Texas, because of weather patterns and geographical location.

12a.
```
          x
 x     x  x x     x  x     x  x  x
 +--+--+--+--+--+--+--+--+--+--+--+
 0  1  2  3  4  5  6  7  8  9 10 11
```

12b. Answers will vary. Sample answer:
1. Did any countries win the same number of gold medals?
2. How many countries won more than three gold medals?
3. How many gold medals did the countries win altogether?

14.
```
<----●--●--●--+--+--+--+--+-->
    -5 -4 -3 -2 -1  0  1  2
```

16. 1860

18. 62

2–3 Adding and Subtracting Integers
Pages 89–92

1. A zero pair of counters has equal amounts of positive and negative counter, therefore there are equal pairs of opposites and they will add to zero, which shows the additive inverse property.

3a. Sample answers: On a number line, start at zero. Move left three spaces to -3. Then move left one space to add -1. The sum is -4.

3b. On a number line, start at zero. Move right five spaces to $+5$. Then move left seven spaces to add -7. The sum is -2.

2. Sample answer: -2; Start at zero. The absolute value is two places to the right.

4a. 0

4b. 0

3c. On a number line, start at zero. Move right four spaces to +4. Then move nine spaces to the left to subtract 9. The difference is −5.

3d. On a number line, start at zero. Move right six spaces to +6. Subtracting −5 is the same as adding +5. So move right five more spaces to add +5. The sum is 11.

5. −3 + 5 = 2

6. −5

7. −7, 7

8. 20, 20

9. 0, 0

10. −20

11. −4

12. −21

13. −11

14. 10

15. 0

16. −21y

17. 40c

18. −15d

19. −4

20. 10

21. 3

22. $\begin{bmatrix} 7 & 0 \\ 4 & 6 \end{bmatrix}$

23. $\begin{bmatrix} -1 & 4 \\ 6 & -6 \end{bmatrix}$

24a. −125°F

24b. −200 (−125) = 325

25. −12, 12

26. 45, 45

27. 302, 302

28. 2

29. 0

30. 23

31. −32

32. 39

33. −16

34. −88

35. −70

36. −22

37. −15

38. 3

39. −5

40. 12t

41. 40b

42. −19w

43. −29p

44. 7y

45. 26d

46. 10

47. −4

48. 10

49. −15

50. 9

51. 5

53. 8

55. 99

57. -59

59. $\begin{bmatrix} 0 & 3 \\ 2 & 2 \end{bmatrix}$

61. $\begin{bmatrix} -4 & -5 \\ -4 & -5 \\ 10 & -3 \end{bmatrix}$

63. 24th floor

52. 2

54. -27

56. 136

58. $\begin{bmatrix} 3 & 7 \\ 1 & -5 \end{bmatrix}$

60. $\begin{bmatrix} 4 & 12 \\ -6 & -1 \end{bmatrix}$

62. 10 units

64a.

3	4	−1
−2	2	6
5	0	1

64b.

2	−1	−6
−7	−3	1
0	−5	−4

64c.

−6	−5	−10
−11	−7	−3
−4	−9	−8

65a.

Monday

	Sesame	Poppy	Blue	Plain
East Store	120	80	64	75
West Store	65	105	77	53

Tuesday

	Sesame	Poppy	Blue	Plain
East Store	112	76	56	74
West Store	69	95	82	50

65b.

Monday + Tuesday

	Sesame	Poppy	Blue	Plain
East Store	232	156	120	149
West Store	134	200	159	103

65c.

Monday − Tuesday

	Sesame	Poppy	Blue	Plain
East Store	8	4	8	1
West Store	−4	10	−5	3

This matrix represents the difference between Monday's and Tuesday's sales in each category.

67a. from 100 to 146

66a. $-7, +2, -3, -1$

66b. -9

66c. Under; yes, it is better than par 72.

68. $4 + (-6) = -2$

67b.

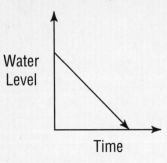

67c. yes; 114

67d. Siberian Elm; American Elm

69.

Water Level

Time

70. commutative $(+)$

71. $55y^2$

72. multiplicative property of zero

73. symmetric $(=)$

74. $6\frac{3}{4}$

75. 14, 20, 29, 34, 37, 38, 43, 59, 64, 74, 84

76. 39

77. 24

78. $n + 33$

2–4 Rational Numbers
Pages 96–99

1. Sample answer: $\frac{1}{2}$, $\frac{10}{3}$, 0.32

2. none

3. One way is to represent these numbers as decimals and then find three decimal values between 0.2 and 0.25, such as 0.21 or 0.24, and then convert these back into fraction form. Another way is to use the calculator to find the mean of the two decimal equivalents. That is one in-between value. Then find the mean of the first decimal and the new value for the second value and mean of the second decimal and the new value for the third value.

4. A fraction cannot have zero in the denominator because that would make the fraction undefined.

5. Yes; since $\frac{a}{b} < \frac{c}{d}$ then what needs to be shown is that $\frac{a}{b} < \frac{a+c}{b+d} < \frac{c}{d}$. If $\frac{a}{b} < \frac{c}{d}$, then $ad < bc$ and then adding ab to both sides, $ad + ab < bc + ab$. Then $a(d + b) < b(c + a)$ and $\frac{a}{b} < \frac{a+c}{b+d}$. The same method can be done to show the other side also. Have students show that side.

7. $<$

9. $=$

11. $-0.5, \frac{3}{4}, \frac{7}{8}, 2.5$

13. See students' work.

15. $>$

17. $<$

19. $<$

21. $>$

23. $\frac{3}{8}, \frac{2}{3}, \frac{6}{7}$

25. $\frac{3}{23}, \frac{8}{42}, \frac{4}{14}$

27. $-\frac{2}{5}, -0.2, 0.2$

29. a 16-ounce drink for $0.59

31. a package of 75 paper plates for $3.29

33. Sample answer: $\frac{2}{3}$

35. Sample answer: $\frac{7}{20}$

37. Sample answer: $\frac{1}{6}$

39. $E = \frac{4}{14}$ or $\frac{2}{7}$; $G = \frac{10}{14}$ or $\frac{5}{7}$; $H = \frac{13}{14}$

41. 0.375 inch

6. See students' work.

8. $<$

10. $\frac{1}{6}, \frac{1}{2}, \frac{2}{3}$

12. 3 three-ounce cans for $2.19.

14. $<$

16. $=$

18. $<$

20. $>$

22. $<$

24. $-\frac{6}{17}, -\frac{4}{15}, -\frac{3}{16}$

26. $-\frac{5}{7}, \frac{6}{13}, 6.7$

28. $0.7, \frac{4}{5}, \frac{9}{10}$

30. a 64-ounce bottle for $6.99

32. Sample answer: $\frac{1}{2}$

34. Sample answer: -1

36. Sample answer: $\frac{6}{12}$

38. a

40. $8.2 < 9.8$

42a. 172.4 cm

42b. 179.6 cm

43. −9, 9

44. from 130 to 150 by 5s

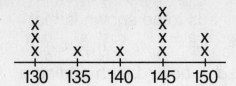

45.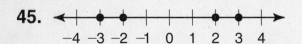

46a. Bryce

46b. Maria

46c. Horizontally the same as Holly and vertically the same as Maria.

47. $m + 2n + \dfrac{3}{2}$

48. 81, 243, 729

49. two times x squared plus six

Self Test
Page 99

1.

```
◄──┼──●──┼──┼──●──┼──●──┼──┼──►
   -4 -3 -2 -1  0  1  2  3  4
```

2.

```
◄──┼──┼──⊕━━┿━━┿━━┿━━┿━━┿━━►
   -4 -3 -2 -1  0  1  2  3  4
```

3. −17

4. −9

5. 55

6. −16

7a.

```
              x
              x
  x       x   x       x  x        x x          x
  ┼───┼───┼───┼───┼───┼───┼───┼──╱╲──┼
 240 250 260 270 280 290 300 310 320 330   370
```

7b. yes; $270

8. <

9. <

10. >

2–5 Adding and Subtracting Rational Numbers
Pages 102–104

1. Sample answer: One method is to add together the numbers of the same sign first and then add the two sums together.

2. See students' work.

3.

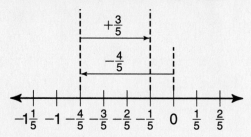

4.

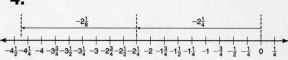

5. $-\dfrac{1}{9}$

6. $\dfrac{1}{4}$

7. $-2\dfrac{5}{8}$

8. -151.8

9. 0.88

10. $\dfrac{2}{5}$

11. 5.75

12. 8

13a. $+\dfrac{1}{2}$

14. $\dfrac{1}{4}$

13b.

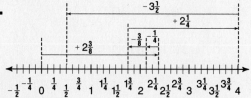

15. $-\dfrac{11}{16}$

16. -5.4

17. -1.3

18. 0

19. $\dfrac{4}{9}$

20. -14.7

21. -0.2007

22. $-\dfrac{5}{28}$

23. $-8\dfrac{5}{8}$

24. 93.4

25. 0.0485

26. 1.01

27. -22.94

28. $1\dfrac{1}{2}$

29. -2.17

30. $\dfrac{7}{20}$

31. 1

32. $-3\dfrac{5}{6}$

33. -3.5

34. -1.3

35. -16.7

36. $\dfrac{8}{15}$

37. $-\dfrac{52}{21}$

38. $\begin{bmatrix} 5.4 & 3 \\ 1 & 7.2 \end{bmatrix}$

39. $\begin{bmatrix} -3.8 & -0.1 \\ 1.7 & 2.9 \end{bmatrix}$

40. $\begin{bmatrix} \dfrac{7}{2} & -7 \\ \dfrac{23}{3} & \dfrac{25}{4} \end{bmatrix}$

41. $\begin{bmatrix} \dfrac{1}{4} & 11 \\ -5 & 8 \\ \dfrac{1}{2} & -12 \end{bmatrix}$

42. $\begin{bmatrix} 1.8 & 2.7 & -9.3 \\ 6 & -9 & 0 \end{bmatrix}$

43. Answers will vary. Sample answer:

$\begin{bmatrix} 5 & 3 \\ 1 & 7 \end{bmatrix}, \begin{bmatrix} 4 & -3 \\ 1 & 2 \end{bmatrix}, \begin{bmatrix} 9 & 0 \\ 2 & 9 \end{bmatrix}, \begin{bmatrix} 18 & 0 \\ 4 & 18 \end{bmatrix}; \begin{bmatrix} 5 & 3 \\ 1 & 7 \end{bmatrix} + \begin{bmatrix} 4 & -3 \\ 1 & 2 \end{bmatrix} = \begin{bmatrix} 9 & 0 \\ 2 & 9 \end{bmatrix} =$

$\begin{bmatrix} 4 & -3 \\ 1 & 2 \end{bmatrix} + \begin{bmatrix} 5 & 3 \\ 1 & 7 \end{bmatrix} \left(\begin{bmatrix} 5 & 3 \\ 1 & 7 \end{bmatrix} + \begin{bmatrix} 4 & -3 \\ 1 & 2 \end{bmatrix} \right) + \begin{bmatrix} 9 & 0 \\ 2 & 9 \end{bmatrix} = \begin{bmatrix} 18 & 0 \\ 4 & 18 \end{bmatrix} =$

$\begin{bmatrix} 5 & 3 \\ 1 & 7 \end{bmatrix} + \left(\begin{bmatrix} 4 & -3 \\ 1 & 2 \end{bmatrix} + \begin{bmatrix} 9 & 0 \\ 2 & 9 \end{bmatrix} \right)$

44. Yes—the amount needed is $1\dfrac{3}{20}$ rolls which is less than $1\dfrac{1}{2}$.

45a. 9.01, 10.13, 11.25

45b. 1.12

45c. $-2, -\dfrac{5}{4}, -\dfrac{1}{2}, \dfrac{1}{4}, 1; -2\dfrac{1}{2}$

46. 48 feet $1\dfrac{1}{4}$ inches

47. $<$

48. -5

49a.

49b. no

50. 11 slices

51. multiplicative property of 0

52. 52

53. $\dfrac{7}{24}$

54. 4096

1a. *ab* is positive if *a* and *b* have the same signs, either both positive or both negative.

1b. *ab* is negative if *a* and *b* have opposite signs, one is negative and the other is positive.

1c. *ab* is equal to 0 if either *a* or *b* is 0, or both *a* and *b* are 0.

3. $a + a^2$

5. -18

7. 24

9. $-\dfrac{4}{5}$

11. -4

13. $-46st$

15. $\begin{bmatrix} -6 & 12 \\ -3 & 15 \end{bmatrix}$

17. $28.65

19. -60

21. -1

23. 2

25. 0.00879

27. $-\dfrac{6}{5}$

29. $-\dfrac{9}{17}$

31. 85.7095

33. 3

35. -6

37. $\dfrac{13}{12}$

39. $-\dfrac{179}{24}$

2a. If a^2 is positive, then *a* is either positive or negative.

2b. If a^3 is positive, then *a* is positive.

2c. If a^3 is negative, then *a* is negative.

4. $2 \times (-3) = -6$

6. 32

8. $\dfrac{49}{9}$

10. $-\dfrac{12}{35}$

12. $-\dfrac{1}{6}$

14. $-27xy$

16. $\begin{bmatrix} 5 & 0 \\ -22.5 & -40 \\ -16 & 20 \end{bmatrix}$

18. 78

20. 42

22. $\dfrac{1}{3}$

24. 360

26. 60

28. $\dfrac{3}{8}$

30. 0.4125

32. 0

34. -24

36. -4

38. $-\dfrac{17}{6}$

40. $-\dfrac{1}{9}$

Algebra 1

41. $\frac{25}{24}$

42. $6ac - 36yr$

43. $-30rt + 4s$

44. $-33mn$

45. $21x$

46. $18bc + 63ab$

47. $16.48x - 5.3y$

48. $\begin{bmatrix} 7 & -57.4 & 0 \\ -28 & -39.2 & 7 \\ -22.4 & -49 & -49 \end{bmatrix}$

49. $\begin{bmatrix} 2 & -6 & 3 \\ \frac{5}{2} & 5 & 1 \end{bmatrix}$

50. $\begin{bmatrix} 5.2 & -8 & -16 \\ 2 & -1.2 & 20 \\ 26.4 & 8.4 & -32 \end{bmatrix}$

51. $\begin{bmatrix} -9 & 22.68 \\ -22.4 & -10 \\ 28.8 & -11.12 \end{bmatrix}$

52. $\begin{bmatrix} -1.6 & -36 \\ 11.2 & 24 \\ -24 & -19.2 \\ 56 & 25.6 \end{bmatrix}$

53. $\begin{bmatrix} 6 & 18 & 4 \\ 0 & 2 & \frac{8}{3} \end{bmatrix}$

54. It is positive.

55. It is negative.

56a. $\frac{1}{9}, \frac{1}{27}, \frac{1}{81}$

56b. $\frac{1}{3}$

56c. $-6, -3, -1.5, -0.75, -0.375,$ -11.625

57a. No; it meets the requirement that no dimensions can be less than 20 feet, but the minimum of 1250 square feet is not met because this yard would have 1216 square feet.

57b. No; it meets the requirement that yards must have a minimum of 1250 square feet because it would have 1330 square feet, but the requirement that no dimension can be less than 20 feet is not met because it has a side of length 19 feet.

57c. Answers will vary. Sample answer: 30 feet

58. $1\frac{1}{5}$ feet

59. -2.2

61. -20

63. -7

65. $\{6, 7\}$

67. 408

60. $>$

62. from 1 to 15 by 1s

64. $5(x + y) - z$ or $5(x + y - z)$

66a. stem 13, leaf 2

66b. stem 35, leaf 7

66c. stem 153, leaf 4

68. 4^3; 64 cubes

2–7 Dividing Rational Numbers
Pages 115–117

1. Both multiplying and dividing rational numbers involve multiplication. In division, you multiply by the reciprocal of the second number.

2. multiplying by the reciprocal

3. Sample answer: $x = \dfrac{1}{2}$

4. Miguel is correct.
$$-\frac{4}{5} = (-1)\frac{4}{5} = \frac{(-1)4}{5} =$$
$$\left(\frac{1}{-1}\right)\frac{4}{5} = \frac{4}{-5}; \frac{-4}{-5} = \frac{(-1)4}{(-1)5}$$
$$= \left(\frac{-1}{-1}\right)\left(\frac{4}{5}\right) = (1)\frac{4}{5} = \frac{4}{5}$$

5. -4

6. -7

7. $-\dfrac{3}{32}$

8. $\dfrac{2}{27}$

9. $-\dfrac{5}{48}$

10. $9s$

11. $-6x$

12. $b + 2$

13. about 2 minutes

14. -9

15. 6

16. $\dfrac{153}{10}$

17. $-\dfrac{1}{18}$

18. 8

19. $-\dfrac{1}{16}$

20. -2

21. -6

22. 12

Algebra 1

23. $-\frac{1}{12}$

24. $\frac{1}{12}$

25. $\frac{243}{10}$

26. $-\frac{1}{12}$

27. $-\frac{35}{3}$

28. $-\frac{35}{2}$

29. $-65m$

30. $-9c$

31. $r + 3$

32. $a + 4$

33. $-20a - 25b$

34. $x + 2y$

35. $-14c + 6d$

36. $-f - 2g$

37. $-a - 4b$

38. 4

39. -1.2

40. $0.\overline{6}$

41. $-0.8\overline{3}$

42. -0.3

43. 4

44a. You would get an error since you are asking the calculator to divide by 0 and this is undefined.

44b. You will end up with the original number since you reciprocated and then reciprocated again. If n is even, you will get the original number. If n is odd, you will get the reciprocal of the number.

44c. 1; You multiplied a number by its reciprocal, which always results in a product of 1.

46. If they buy them each individually, the total cost will be $113.47 ($\frac{1}{5}$ off each pair). If Sharon buys the two most expensive pairs and LaShondra buys the next two most expensive pairs and then one of them buys the fifth pair by itself, the total cost will be $110.37. Therefore, the latter is how they would buy the shoes.

45a.

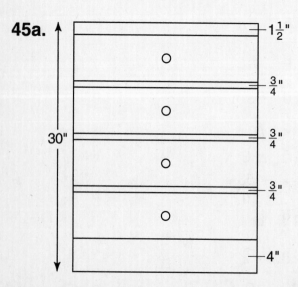

45b. $5\frac{9}{16}$ inches

47. $4\frac{1}{20}$ inches

48. $\frac{3}{5}$

49. $\frac{13}{12}$

50. Sample answer: $\frac{19}{24}$

51a. $\begin{bmatrix} -2 & 4 \\ 3 & 12 \end{bmatrix}$

51b. $\begin{bmatrix} 4 & 4 \\ 7 & 2 \end{bmatrix}$

52a. 131

52b.

52c. yes, 472

53. $20b + 24$

54. $\frac{5}{4}$

55a.

Stem	Leaf
13	0
15	4
17	2 3
19	4
20	0
22	0 2
24	5
25	1 4
27	9
29	0
30	4 7
33	0
34	6
52	5

$13 \mid 0 = 13{,}000$

55b. $13,000

55c. $52,500

55d. 9

Algebra 1

2–8 Square Roots and Real Numbers
Pages 122–125

1. Sample answer:

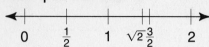

2. The comic is funny because you usually count off by natural numbers {1, 2, 3, 4, . . . } not square roots.

3. yes; rational, integers, whole, natural

4. $3(3) = 9$ and $(-3)(-3) = 9$.

5. $x \leq 0$

6. Sample answer: A rational number is a number that can be expressed as a common fraction. An irrational number is a number that cannot be expressed as a common fraction.

7. 8

8. -6

9. 11.05

10. ± 0.28

11. 16

12. 12.29

13. Q

14. Q, Z, W, N

15. Q

16. I

17. ← | | | | | ○ | | | →
   2 3 4 5 6 7 8 9 10

18. ← | | | | ● | | | | | | →
   −6 −5 −4 −3 −2 −1 0 1 2

19. ← | | | | ○ | | | | →
   −2 −1 0 1 2 3 4 5 6

20. 45

21. 13

22. 0.07

23. $\frac{2}{3}$

24. -17

25. 20.49

26. $\frac{5}{8}$

27. 15

28. ± 34.03

29. -25

30. 1.4

31. $\frac{3}{5}$

32. -2.41

33. 9.33

34. ± 23

35. -47

36. 8.89

37. -20

38. ± 4

39. Z, Q

40. W, Z, Q

41. Q

42. Q

43. Q

44. N, W, Z, Q

45. Q

46. N, W, Z, Q

47. I

48. Q

49. Q

50. N, W, Z, Q

51. (number line: open circle at −2, arrow left; marks −6 −5 −4 −3 −2 −1 0 1 2)

52. (number line: open circle at 1, arrow right; marks −3 −2 −1 0 1 2 3 4 5)

53. (number line: closed circle at −4, arrow right; marks −7 −6 −5 −4 −3 −2 −1 0 1)

54. (number line: open circle at 6, arrow left; marks 2 3 4 5 6 7 8 9 10)

55. (number line: open circle at −12, arrow left; marks −15 −14 −13 −12 −11 −10 −9 −8 −7)

56. (number line: closed circle at 4.5, arrow left; marks 0 1 2 3 4 5 6 7 8)

57. (number line: closed circle at −5.2, arrow left; marks −5.4 −5.3 −5.2 −5.1 −5.0 −4.9)

58. (number line: open circle at 3/4, arrow left; marks 1/4 0 1/4 1/2 3/4 1 1 1/4 1 1/2 1 3/4)

59. (number line: closed circle at 5 3/4, arrow left; marks 4 1/2 4 3/4 5 5 1/4 5 1/2 5 3/4 6 6 1/4 6 1/2)

60. 3.16 cm × 3.16 cm × 10 cm

61. Yes, it lies between 27 and 28.

62a. $\sqrt{10}$, $\sqrt{11}$, $\sqrt{12}$, $\sqrt{13}$, $\sqrt{14}$, and $\sqrt{15}$

62b. $\sqrt{28}$, $\sqrt{29}$, and $\sqrt{30}$

63. about 50 miles

64. about 31 mph

65. Fibonacci

66a. 103 or more cases

66b. (number line: closed circle at 103, arrow right; marks 98 99 100 101 102 103 104 105 106)

67. −12

68. $-\dfrac{1}{24}$

69. a 1-pound package of lunch meat for $1.95

70. 1

71. from 500 to 520 by 5s

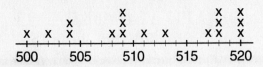

72. (number line: closed circles at 0, 2, and 6; marks −1 0 1 2 3 4 5 6 7)

73. Graph b

74. associative (+)

75a. to the nearest ten-thousand

76. 24

75b. 10

75c. $690,000

77. 26, 32

78. p^6

2–9 Problem Solving: Write Equations and Formulas
Pages 129–132

1. Answers will vary. Sample answers: How much does her normal heart rate have to increase to reach her target heart rate? During the entire workout, how much does her heart rate decrease? During the entire workout, how much does her heart rate increase?

2. A formula is a type of equation that states a rule for the relationship between certain quantities.

3. Answers will vary. Sample answer: If José has a garden with the dimensions of 20 feet by 30 feet, what is the area?

4. See students' work.

5a. 4 points

5b. 15 questions

5c. 86

5d. 6 points

5e. $15 - n$

5f. $4n$

6. $2x + 3y = 13$

7. $n + 5 \geq 48$

8. $P = 2(a + b)$

9. Let s = average speed; $s = \dfrac{189}{3} = 63$

10. Let q = number of quarters; $q + (q + 4) + (q + 4 - 7) = 28$

11. The product of a times the sum of y and 1 is b.

12. Answers will vary. Sample answer: Your mother works 8 less than 5 times the number of hours that you work during the summer. How many hours did your mother work if you worked 20 hours this week?

13a. 640 feet

13b. $y - 80$

13c. $\ell + \ell + w + w$ or $2\ell + 2w$

13d. 200 ft

13e. 24,000 ft²

14. $V = \dfrac{1}{3}Bh$

13f. Is there enough space to build the playground as designed?

15. $a^2 + b^3 = 25$

16. $\dfrac{x}{y} > 18 + 5(x + y)$

17. $x < (a - 4)^2$

18. $C = 2\pi r$

19. $\dfrac{7}{8}(a + b + c^2) = 48$

20. Sample answer: $t =$ how many tapes Nicole has. $25 - t =$ how many CDs Nicole has.
$$4 + \frac{1}{2}t = 25 - t \text{ or}$$
$$4 + 1\frac{1}{2}t = 25$$

21. Sample answer:
$x =$ first number
$x + 25 =$ second number
$25 + 2x = 106$

22. Sample answer:
$2D =$ Anna's age
$D =$ Dennis' age
$D - 4 =$ Curtis' age
$2D + D + D - 4 = 32$

23. Sample answer:
$y =$ how much money Hector saves
$y = 2(7)(50)$ or $y = 14(50)$

24. The square of the product of m and n is equal to p.

25. V is equal to the quotient of a times h and three.

26. The quantity of the sum of a and two, divided by five is greater than ten.

27. Sample answer: Three times the number of miles home is from school is 36. How many miles away from home is the school?

28. Sample answer: Manny's Suits for Men is having a $25.00 off sale. If the original cost of a suit is p, find the original cost of the suit if the sale price is $150.00.

29. Sample answer: The number of hours spent waiting for a doctor in the waiting room is 5 minutes more than 6 times the number of appointments she has. How long would you have to wait for a doctor with d appointments?

30. $a^2 - b^2$

31. $ab + cd + 2d - 8$

32. $s^2 + \pi \cdot \dfrac{s^2}{2}$

33. Sample answer:
$$4.5 + x + x = 24 + x$$
$$x = 19.5$$

34a. What is the area of the two 7-inch pizzas and what is the area of one 12-inch pizza?

34b. See students' work.

34c. $A = \pi r^2$
(two 7-inch pizzas)
$A = \pi(3.5)^2$
$A = 12.25\pi$ or ≈ 38.5 in² each
2 pizzas ≈ 77 in²
(one 12-inch pizza)
$A = \pi(6)^2$
$A = 36\pi$ or ≈ 113.1 in²
One 12-inch pizza is the best buy.

34d. If crust were a factor, you would have to take circumference into consideration and figure how the circumferences compare.

35a. $A = \frac{1}{2}h(a + b)$

35b. $A = 108\frac{1}{2}$ ft²

36a.

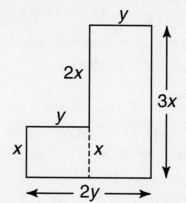

36b. $6x + 4y$

36c. $A = xy + 3xy$ or $A = 4xy$

36d. Perimeter = 49 cm
Area = 88 cm²

37. -8

38. 12

39. $\begin{bmatrix} 8 & -1.6 \\ 1 & \end{bmatrix}$

40. Sample answer: $\frac{20}{42}$

41. $-25, 25$

42. c

43. {2, 3, 4, 5}

1. b

2. See students' work.

3. $x - 1.2 = 3.3$
    $4.5 - 1.2 \overset{?}{=} 3.3$
    $3.3 = 3.3$

4. 34

5. $x + (-5) = -10; x = -5$

6. -3

7. -17

8. -19.9

9. -12

10. $-\frac{1}{2}$

11. -14

12. $n - 13 = -5; 8$

13. $n + (-56) = -82; -26$

14. -32

15. -9

16. -24

17. -1.3

18. -9

19. 1.4

20. 15

21. -3

22. -4

23. -6

24. -2.8

25. -7

26. 2.32

27. 24

28. -3.6

29. $1\frac{1}{4}$

30. $-\frac{1}{6}$

31. $-\frac{1}{10}$

32. $23 - n = 42; -19$

33. $n + 5 = 34; 29$

34. $n - 45 = -78; -33$

35. $n - (-23) = 35; 12$

36. $n + (-45) = 77; 122$

37. $n + (-35) = 98; 133$

38. yes; $n^2 = 25; n = \pm 5$

39a. 19,096,400 more subscribers

40a. $10.83

39b. Sample answer: 25 million

40b. $20.60

41a. 24 years old

42. 16

41b. 24 years

41c. 78 years

41d. 34 years old

41e. 24 years

43. -5

44. 76

45. $-0.73x$

46. $30a + 6b$

47. 48

3–2 Solving Equations with Multiplication and Division
Pages 152–154

1. Doralina is correct. There is no value for x that would make the statement $0x = 8$ true.

2. Rise is the number of units in a vertical direction, and run is the number of units in a horizontal direction.

3. 360 inches or 30 feet

4.

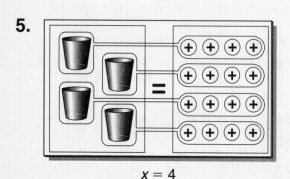

Let x = width. Then $17x = 51$, and $x = 3$.

5.

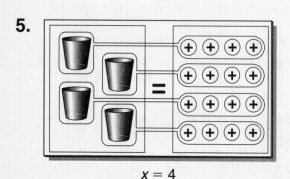

$x = 4$

6. -7

7. 17

8. 0.19

9. 48

10. 70

11. $\frac{11}{15}$

12. $8n = 216$; 27

13. $-7n = 1.477$; -0.211

14. 7

15. -9

16. 4.44 or $4\frac{4}{9}$

17. -17.33 or $-17\frac{1}{3}$

18. -3.67 or $-3\frac{2}{3}$

19. -14

20. -23

21. 12.81

22. -17

23. 600

24. 55

25. -275

26. 112

27. -25

28. $-30\frac{6}{11}$

29. $8\frac{6}{13}$

30. $1\frac{5}{9}$

31. -8

32. $6n = -96$; -16

33. $-12n = -156$; 13

34. $\frac{1}{4}n = -16.325$; -65.3

35. $\frac{4}{3}n = 4.82$; 3.615

36. $\frac{7}{8}n = 14$; 16

37. 45

38. 23

39. 30

41. 12

43a. 50 people; 83 people

43b. 455 people

45a. 23 minutes

45b. $1.80

47. $17 + 1\frac{1}{2}y = 33\frac{1}{2}$

49. $\frac{19}{28}$

51a. The number of bags increased during the day.

51b. The machine was refilled.

51c. See students' work.

53. 31

40. $-\frac{1}{3}$

42. No; if x is negative, then $-x$ is positive.

44. 13,312,667

46. -19

48. 51,173 slices

50.

52. $15x - 10y$

3–3 Solving Multi-Step Equations
Pages 159–161

1a. Divide each term by 2.

1b. Fractions would be introduced.

2. Let $2n$ and $2n + 2$ represent consecutive even numbers and let $2n + 1$ and $2n + 3$ represent consecutive odd numbers.

$$2n + 2n + 2 = (2n + 1) + (2n + 3)$$
$$4n + 2 = 4n + 4$$
$$2 = 4$$

Since this is not a true statement, the sum of two consecutive even numbers can never equal the sum of two consecutive odd numbers.

3. Subtract 2; $n - 2$

4.
$$4x + 3x - 5 = 27$$
$$4(-2) + 3(-2) - 5 \stackrel{?}{=} 27$$
$$-8 + (-6) - 5 \stackrel{?}{=} 27$$
$$-19 \neq 27$$

5. $-22, -20, -18$

6. 2

7. $3x + 2 = 8$; 2

8. Add 5 to each side, then divide each side by 4; 5.

9. Subtract 7 from each side, then divide each side by 3; −6.

10. Add 6 to each side, then multiply each side by $\frac{9}{2}$; 90.

11. Subtract 3 from each side, then multiply each side by −7; 35.

12. Multiply each side by 7, then add 3 to each side; −11.

13. Rewrite the numerator as $p + 5$, multiply each side by −2, and then subtract 5; −17.

14. $n + (n + 1) = -31$; −16, −15

15. $n + (n + 2) + (n + 4) = 21$; 5, 7, 9

16. $29 = 13 + 4n$; $n = 4$

17. −1

18. −2

19. −2

20. 1.25 or $1\frac{1}{4}$

21. −42.72

22. 28

23. $12\frac{2}{3}$

24. −56

25. −6

26. −125

27. −48

28. −126

29. 30

30. −8

31. 57

32. −14.5

33. $4\frac{3}{7}$

34. $25\frac{1}{3}$

35. $12 - 2n = -7$; $9\frac{1}{2}$

36. $n + (n + 1) + (n + 2) = -33$; −12, −11, −10

37. $n + (n + 1) + (n + 2) + (n + 3) = 86$; 20, 21, 22, 23

38. $n + (n + 2) = 196$; 97, 99

39. $n + (n + 2) + (n + 4) = 39$; 11 m, 13 m, 15 m

40. $2n + (n + 6) = 120$; 38 in., 40 in., 42 in., 44 in.

41. 28

42. 4.793

43. −38

44. −16.67 or $-16\frac{2}{3}$

45. $(3n - 1) + (3n + 1) + (3n + 3)$

46a. $(120 - 5) + (d - 5) = 192$; 82 days

46b.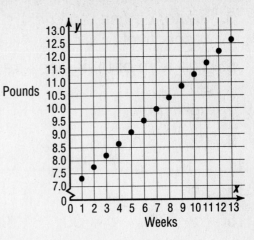

47. $2a + 2 = 26$; 12 letters

48. Wilson, 16 bags; Martinez, 8 bags; Brightfeather, 4 bags; Wimberly, 2 bags

49a–b. See students' work.

50. 9

51. I

52. $-4x$

53. -5

54. substitution (=)

55. 5

56. $8\frac{1}{2}$

Self Test
Page 161

1. 44

2. 58

3. 6

4. -1885

5. $-8\frac{1}{3}$

6. 25

7. $23 - n = 42$; -19

8. $34w = 68$; 2 cm

9. $n + (n + 2) = 126$; 62, 64

10. $p = 10(5.05) - 3.50$; $47

3–4 Integration: Geometry   Angles and Triangles
Pages 165–167

1a. A compliment is an expression of praise. A complement is something that completes or fills.

1b. The word *complement* has the mathematical meaning.

2. A supplement is something added to complete something, make up for a deficiency, or extend to strengthen the whole. The supplement of an angle completes a 180° angle, which is a straight line.

3. acute, obtuse, and right, respectively

4. See students' work.

5. The sum of their measures is 90°.

6. none, 50°

7. 79°, 169°

8. 66°, 156°

9. $(90 - 3x)°, (180 - 3x)°$

10. $(50 - 2x)°, (140 - 2x)°$

11. $(110 - x)°, (200 - x)°$

12. 122°

13. 85°

14. $(160 - 2x)°$

15. $(c - 38) + c = 90; 26°, 64°$

16. $x + (x + 5) + (2x + 3) = 180;$ 43°, 48°, 89°

17. 48°, 138°

18. 3°, 93°

19. none, 55°

20. none, 90°

21. 69°, 159°

22. none, 6°

23. none, 81°

24. $(90 - y)°, (180 - y)°$

25. $(90 - 3a)°, (180 - 3a)°$

26. $(60 - x)°, (150 - x)°$

27. $(128 - b)°, (218 - b)°$

28. $z°, (90 + z)°$

29. 70°

30. 60°

31. 105°

32. 19°

33. 138°

34. $180 - (x + y)°$ or $(180 - x - y)°$

35. $(190 - 2p)°$

36. $(179 - 3c)°$

37. 45°

38. $37 + 37 + x = 180; 37°, 106°$

39. $x + (x - 30) = 180; 75°$

40. $53 + 37 + x = 180; 90°$

41. $x + (30 + 3x) = 90; 15°, 75°$

42. $x + 2x = 180; 60°$

43. $x + 3x + 4x = 180; 22.5°, 67.5°, 90°$

44. See students' work.

45. 60°

46a. 87°

46b. 72°

46c. shuttle

47. 40°

48. 5

49a. $80

50. 8

49b. $74.75

51. $7t$

52. $-28y$

53a.

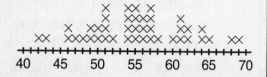

54. commutative $(+)$

53b. yes; 51, 54, 55, and 57

55.

Stem	Leaf
4	2 3 6 6 7 8 9 9
5	0 0 1 1 1 1 2 4
	4 4 4 5 5 5 5 6
	6 6 7 7 7 7 8
6	0 1 1 1 2 2 4 4
	5 8 9

$5\,|\,2 = 52$

3–5 Solving Equations with the Variable on Both Sides
Pages 170–172

1a. Sample answer: women are training harder, working out more, and so on.

1b. Sample answer:

Year	Men	Women
1928	111.8	136.8
1948	109.3	130.2
1968	106.7	123.5
1988	104.2	116.9
2008	101.6	110.2
2028	99.1	103.6
2048	96.6	97.0
2068	94.0	90.3

1c. Answers may vary.

3. Carmen; you begin with the numerals in the innermost grouping symbols—in this case, $(x - 1)$.

5. $-\frac{1}{2}$; Add $4x$ to each side, subtract 10 from each side, then divide each side by 14.

2. An identity is true for *all* values of the variable. An equation with no solution is true for *no* values of the variable.

4. See students' work.

6. $\frac{12}{11}$; Add $3y$ to each side, add 10 to each side, then divide each side by 11.

7. -25; Subtract $\frac{1}{5}x$ from each side, subtract 3 from each side, then multiply by $\frac{5}{2}$.

8. 2.5; Subtract $5.4y$ from each side, add 2.8 to each side, then divide each side by 4.4.

9. all numbers; Distribute the 5 on the right side, combine terms. Since the expressions on each side of the equation are the same, the equation is an identity.

10. 3; Multiply 4 by $(2x - 1)$ and -10 by $(x - 5)$. Subtract $8x$ from each side, and subtract 50 from each side. Then divide each side by -18.

11. $2(n + 2) = 3n - 13$; 17, 19

12. $6x + (x - 3) + (3x + 7) = 180$; $105.6°, 14.6°, 59.8°$

13. $\frac{1}{2}n + 16 = \frac{2}{3}n - 4$; 120

14. 10

15. no solution

16. 1.83 or $1\frac{5}{6}$

17. -2

18. 0.925

19. 5.6

20. no solution

21. -16

22. 3.57 or $3\frac{4}{7}$

23. no solution

24. -17

25. 4

26. no solution

27. 2.6 or $2\frac{3}{5}$

28. -3

29. 8

30. 3.6 or $3\frac{3}{5}$

31. 2

32. 42

33. all numbers

34. $3(n + 4) = 2n + 38$; 26, 28, 30

35. $\frac{1}{5}n + 5n = 7n - 18$; 10

36. $\frac{2}{5}(n + 12) = 6 + \frac{1}{3}(n)$; 18, 30

37. $n + (n + 2) + (n + 4) = 180$; $58°, 60°, 62°$

38. $x + (x + 30) + 3[x + (x + 30)] = 180$; $7.5°, 37.5°, 135°$

39a. $4x + 6 = 4x + 6$; identity

39b. $5x - 7 = x + 3$; 2.5

39c. $-3x + 6 = 3x - 6$; 2

39d. $5.4x + 6.8 = 4.6x + 2.8$; -5

39e. $2x - 8 = 2x - 6$; no solution

40. 84 years old

41a. 6.827 years

41b. Air conditioner sales are decreasing while fan sales are increasing.

42. 17.5 years

43. $148°$

44. 54

45. -2.7

46. $10 + x = 0.9(15 + x)$, 35 years

47. $\dfrac{11}{9}$

48. As students spend more time watching TV, their test scores go down.

49. 11.05

3–6 Solving Equations and Formulas
Pages 175–177

1a. $\dfrac{7y + z}{a} = m$

2. The larger heel absorbs a greater amount of pressure.

3. See students' work.

4. $\dfrac{7 + 4y}{3}$

5. $\dfrac{3x - 7}{4}$

6. $\dfrac{b}{a} - 1$

7. $\dfrac{c - b}{2}$

8. $\dfrac{Fd^2}{Gm}$

9. $\dfrac{2S - nt}{n}$

10. $2x + 12 = 3y - 31; \dfrac{2x + 43}{3}$

11. $\dfrac{b}{9}$

12. $\dfrac{3z + 2y}{e}$

13. $3c - a$

14. $\dfrac{5(b - a)}{3}$

15. $\dfrac{v - r}{t}$

16. $\dfrac{y - b}{x}$

17. $\dfrac{I}{pt}$

18. $\dfrac{3c - 2}{b}$

19. $\dfrac{H}{0.24I^2t}$

20. $\dfrac{E^2}{P}$

21. $\dfrac{-t + 5}{4}$

22. $\dfrac{6y - 5x}{k}$

23. $\dfrac{4}{3}(c - b)$

24. $\dfrac{-2 - p}{p}$

25. $\dfrac{5x + y}{2}$

26. $\dfrac{-20 + n}{3a}$

27. $2x + 12 = 3y - 31; \dfrac{3y - 43}{2}$

28. $\dfrac{5}{8}x = \dfrac{1}{2}y + 3; \dfrac{5}{4}x - 6$

29. $\dfrac{2}{3}x + 5 = \dfrac{1}{2}y - 3; \dfrac{3}{4}y - 12$

30. $\dfrac{9}{5}C + 32 = 2C + 30; 10°$ C or $50°$ F

31. $900

32. 82.8 meters

33a. 36 words per minute

34. 3

33b. Clarence, with 74 words per
minute

35. $5°$

36. 6:35 A.M.

37. $x \neq 2$

38. 4

39. {8}

40. See students' work.

3–7 Integration: Statistics   Measures of Central Tendency
Pages 181–183

1. The mean is affected by extreme values, where the median is not. Mode is affected by the amount of repetition of values.

2. The mean, since it finds the average amount of the contributions. The mean is affected by extreme values.

3. Count the total number of x's. To find the mean, multiply the number by the number of x's in that column. Then divide by the total number of x's (4.8). To find the median, divide the total number of x's by 2 (13 ÷ 2 or ≈ 7) and count from left to right. The seventh x represents the median (4). The mode is the number with the greatest number of x's in its column (2).

4. Mode, since the data are nonnumeric, the mean and median would have no meaning in this context.

5. See students' work.

6. middle

7. median

8. mean

9. mode

10. 7; 6; none

11. 8.2; 8; 8

12. 93.77; 94; 82

13. Sample answer: 20, 20, 30, 50, 90, 90

14. Sample answer: 65, 65, 70, 70, 73, 77

15a. 3.857; 3; 3

16. $8\frac{1}{6}$; 8; none

15b. The mean, it is affected by extreme values.

17. 96.8; 50; none

18. 17.5; 17.5; 23, 12

19. 9; 9; none

20. 8; 7; 7

21. 5.69; 4.56; none

22. 75.3; 77; 77, 88

23. 212.94; 218; 219

25. 14

27a. mean

27b. Yes, because the article indicates that the median value is in the middle of the data set.

27c. No, he should have used the term *mean* since the mean can be affected by extremely high values, causing the majority to be below the mean value.

29. $1660\frac{3}{5}$; $1076\frac{1}{2}$; none

31. 37.5 mph

33. 16

35. −20

37. $5 + 9ac + 14b$

24a. Sample answer: 6, 6, 6, 6, 6, 6, 6, 6, 6, 0

24b. Sample answer: 5, 5, 5, 5, 5, 5, 5, 5, 5, 25

24c. not possible

24d. No, because it is always in the middle of the set of data.

26a. $\frac{6n + 9}{3}$ or $2n + 3$

26b. $2n + 3$

28a. 29.4; 16; none

28b. The mean is most representative.

30. about 798; about 625

32. $\frac{a + 5}{21}$

34. 9

36. 15; substitution (=), substitution (=), identity (×)

1. If the cross products of two ratios in a proportion are equal, then the two ratios are equivalent.

2. Sample answer: In the proportion $\frac{x}{2.5} = \frac{3}{4}$, multiply 2.5 and 3, then divide by 4.

3. See students' work.

4. See students' work.

5. $=$

6. $\neq$

7. 12

8. 20

9. 5

10. 18

11. 4.62

12. 2.25

13. 9.5 gallons

14. $\neq$

15. $=$

16. $=$

17. $\neq$

18. $\neq$

19. $=$

20. 6

21. 9

22. $-\frac{63}{16}$ or -3.938

23. $\frac{8}{5}$ or 1.6

24. 5

25. 0.84

26. 23

27. $-\frac{149}{6}$ or -24.8

28. $\frac{3}{5}$ or 0.6

29. 11

30. 11

31. 2.28

32. 1.232

33. 1.251

34. 63.368

35a.

Louis' age	1	2	3	6	10	20	30
Mariah's age	9	10	11	14	18	28	38

36. 6237 leaps

35b. 9, 5, 3.$\overline{6}$, 2.$\overline{3}$, 1.8, 1.4, 1.2$\overline{6}$

35c. $r = \frac{y + 8}{y}$

35d. The ratio gets smaller.

35e. No, if the ratio equaled 1, Mariah and Louis would be the same age.

37. 85 movies

38. 50 pounds

39. 23; 19; 18

40. $t = \frac{v}{a}$

Algebra 1

41. $4x - 2x = 100; 50$

42. 28

43a. 93

44. 6 under par, or -6

43b. $9695

43c. more than 40

43d. $93 - p$

43e. yes

45. 10

46. $x^2 + \frac{3}{4}x$

4–2 Integration: Geometry Similar Triangles
Pages 203–205

1. $\angle R$ and $\angle U$, $\angle S$ and $\angle T$, $\angle Q$ and $\angle V$

2. Sample answer: The measures of their corresponding sides are proportional, and the measures of their corresponding angles are equal.

3. $\angle R$ and $\angle S$, $\angle E$ and $\angle O$, $\angle D$ and $\angle X$

$\frac{RE}{SO} = \frac{ED}{OX}, \frac{RE}{SO} = \frac{RD}{SX}, \frac{ED}{OX} = \frac{RD}{SX}$

4. See students' work.

5. $\triangle DEF$

6. no

7. yes

8. $o = 20$, $p = 10$

9. $\ell = 12$, $m = 6$

10. $k = 3$, $o = 8$

11. 27 feet high

12. $\triangle PNY$

13. $\triangle DFE$

14. $\triangle RQY$

15. no

16. yes

17. yes

18. no

19. no

20. no

21. $a = \frac{55}{6}$, $b = \frac{22}{3}$

22. $b = \frac{25}{7}$, $c = \frac{30}{7}$

23. $d = \frac{51}{5}$, $e = 9$

24. $d = \frac{112}{13}$, $f = \frac{84}{13}$

25. $a = 2.78$, $c = 4.24$

26. $a = 27$, $b = 24$

27. $b = 16.2$, $d = 6.3$

28. $d = 7$, $e = 10$

29. $c = \frac{7}{2}$, $d = \frac{17}{8}$

30. 4:9

31. Sample answer:

32. 24 inches from pocket B

33a. $\frac{3}{9} = \frac{d}{d + 39}$; $d = 19.5$ ft, yes

34. $3\frac{1}{3}$ inches

33b. When the ball is served from 8 feet, $d = 23.4$ ft and the serve is a fault. When the ball is served from 10 feet, $d = 16.7$ ft. Therefore, tall players have an easier time serving.

35. $16\frac{1}{2}$ feet by 21 feet

36. -12

37. 160

38. -23

39. 60 million; 420 million

40. $<$

41. 23; $(19 - 12) \div 7 \cdot 23$
$= 7 \div 7 \cdot 23$ substitution $(=)$
$= 1 \cdot 23$ substitution $(=)$
$= 23$ multiplicative identity

4–3 Integration: Trigonometry   Trigonometric Ratios
Pages 210–214

1a. 4

1b. 9

2. sine and cosine

3. Use the sine when the opposite side and hypotenuse are known, use the cosine when the adjacent side and the hypotenuse are known, use the tangent when the opposite side and the adjacent side are known.

4. $\angle QRP$; $\angle SPR$

5a. cosine

5b. tangent

5c. sine

6. See students' work.

7. $\sin Y = 0.600$, $\cos Y = 0.800$, $\tan Y = 0.750$

8. $\sin Y \approx 0.946$, $\cos Y \approx 0.324$, $\tan Y \approx 2.917$

9. 0.8192

10. 0.8910

11. 0.1228

12. 16°

13. 46°

14. 68°

15. 36°

16. 10°

17. $m\angle B = 50°$, $AC \approx 12.3$ m, $BC \approx 10.3$ m

18. $m\angle B = 20°$, $AB \approx 9.6$ cm, $AC \approx 3.3$ cm

19. $m\angle A = 30°$, $AC \approx 13.9$ m, $BC = 8$ m

20. about 3.4°

21. $\sin G = 0.6$, $\cos G = 0.8$, $\tan G = 0.75$

22. $\sin G \approx 0.246$, $\cos G \approx 0.969$, $\tan G \approx 0.254$

23. $\sin G \approx 0.471$, $\cos G \approx 0.882$, $\tan G \approx 0.533$

24. $\sin G \approx 0.923$, $\cos G \approx 0.385$, $\tan G = 2.4$

25. $\sin G \approx 0.923$, $\cos G \approx 0.385$, $\tan G = 2.4$

26. $\sin G \approx 0.724$, $\cos G \approx 0.690$, $\tan G = 1.05$

27. 0.3584

28. 0.9659

29. 0.9703

30. 1.4826

31. 0.3746

32. 0.5774

33. 33°

34. 40°

35. 22°

36. 73°

37. 62°

38. 84°

39. 77°

40. 33°

41. 58°

42. 17°

43. 18°

44. 42°

45. $m\angle B = 60°$, $AC \approx 12.1$ m, $BC = 7$ m

46. $m\angle A = 60°$, $AC = 21$ in., $BC \approx 36.4$ in.

47. $m\angle A = 45°$, $AC = 6$ ft, $AB \approx 8.5$ ft

48. $m\angle B = 61°$, $AB \approx 20.6$ m, $BC \approx 10$ m

49. $m\angle A = 63°$, $AC \approx 9.1$ in., $BC \approx 17.8$ in.

50. $m\angle B = 69°$, $AB \approx 13.9$ in., $BC \approx 5.0$ in.

51. $m\angle A \approx 23°$, $m\angle B \approx 67°$, $AB \approx 12.8$ ft

52. $m\angle A \approx 53°$, $m\angle B \approx 37°$, $AB \approx 10$ ft

53. $m\angle A = 30°$, $m\angle B = 60°$, $AC \approx 5.2$ cm

54a. side $C = 5$; angle $A = 36.9°$, angle $B = 53.1°$; $\sin A = 0.600$, $\sin B = 0.800$, $\cos A = 0.800$, $\cos B = 0.600$, $\tan A = 0.750$, $\tan B = 1.333$

54b. side $C = 13$; angle $A = 22.6°$, angle $B = 67.4°$; $\sin A = 0.385$, $\sin B = 0.923$, $\cos A = 0.923$, $\cos B = 0.385$, $\tan A = 0.417$, $\tan B = 2.400$

54c. side $C = 44.7$; angle $A = 26.6°$, angle $B = 63.4°$; sin $A = 0.447$, sin $B = 0.894$, cos $A = 0.894$, cos $B = 0.447$, tan $A = 0.500$, tan $B = 2.000$

54d. side $C = 160.1$; angle $A = 51.3°$, angle $B = 38.7°$; sin $A = 0.781$, sin $B = 0.625$, cos $A = 0.625$, cos $B = 0.781$, tan $A = 1.250$, tan $B = 0.800$

55a. true

55b. false

55c. false

55d. true

55e. true

56. 483 ft

57. 2229 ft

58. 121 m

59. 3

60. 0.264

61. 10

62. $5x = \$47.50$; $\$9.50$

63. N, W, Z, Q

64. $a + 3$

65. $\frac{2}{15}$

66. -21

67. $9x + 2y$

68. 18

69. 125

4–4 Percents
Pages 218–221

1. They are the same.

2. Enter: 57 $\boxed{\text{2nd}}$ $\boxed{\%}$ $\boxed{\times}$ 42 $\boxed{=}$ 23.94

3. The investment at the higher rate may be too risky.

4. The sum of the percents is greater than 100.

5. See students' work.

6. 75%, 0.75

7. 43%, 0.43

8. 8%, 0.08

9. 55%

10. $56\frac{1}{4}\%$; 56.25%

11. 15

12. $21\frac{1}{3}\%$; $21.\overline{3}\%$

13. $52.50

14. $280

15. $1200 at 10%, $6000 at 14%

16. 67%, 0.67

17. 30%, 0.30

18. $62\frac{1}{2}\%$, 0.625

19. 70%, 0.70

20. $83\frac{1}{3}\%$, $0.8\overline{3}$

21. 180%, 1.80

22. $66\frac{2}{3}$%, $0.\overline{6}$

23. $62\frac{1}{2}$%, 0.625

24. 250%, 2.5

25. 50%

26. 30%

27. $12\frac{1}{2}$%, 12.5%

28. 40%

29. 400%

30. 31%

31. 2.5%

32. 14

33. 72.3

34. 40%

35. 702.4

36. 40%

37. 28%

38. $560

39. 25.92

40. 49.3%

41. 12%

42. $432

43. $3125

44. $4\frac{1}{2}$ years

45. $2400

46. $44.\overline{4}$%

47. 39%, 34%, 15%, 12%

48. $3800

49. 11.5%

50.

Desserts Eaten in the Home

kitchen 30%

bedroom 28%

den 10%

living room 18%

dining room 14%

51. $5.45

52. black olives

53a. about 54 people; about 23 people

53b. Respondents could choose more than one entree.

54.

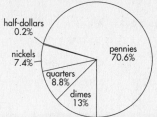

U.S. Coins Minted in 1994

half-dollars 0.2%

nickels 7.4%

quarters 8.8%

dimes 13%

pennies 70.6%

55. about 277 feet tall

56. $b = 6$; $c = 8$

57. $\frac{77}{4}$ or 19.25

58. 8.3, 6.5, 4

59. −4.7

60. 86.7

61. −28y

62.

B
B
B   B   B   B
G   B   B   G   B   G
B   G   G   G   G   G
G   G   G   G   G   G

7.5   8   8.5   9   9.5   10

Hours of Sleep

63. 2

64. 25, 30.5, 36

Self Test
Page 221

1. 5

2. 40

3. 5

4. $x = 15$, $y = 25$

5. $\angle B = 34°$, $b \approx 11.5$, $c \approx 20.5$

6. $\angle A = 37°$, $\angle B \approx 53°$, $c \approx 20$ mm

7. no

8. 80

9. $62\frac{1}{2}\%$, 62.5%

10. 7520 people

4–5 Percent of Change
Pages 224–227

1. Subtract old from new. Divide the result by old. Move decimal point 2 places to the right.

2. Multiply tax rate by original price.

3. $\frac{1773}{17,972} = \frac{r}{100}$

4. See students' work.

5. increase; 40%

6. decrease; 14%

7. decrease; 50%

8. $126.65

9. $85.85

10. $47.93

11. $196

12. decrease; 41%

13. increase; 69%

14. increase; 162%

15. decrease; 55%

16. increase; 42%

17. decrease; 27%

18. decrease; 34%

19. increase; 2%

20. increase; 10%

21. $233.24

22. $35.35

23. $19.90

24. $56.18

25. $85.39

26. $56.02

27. $16.59

28. $39.75

29. $30.09

30a. $60.08; $57.85

30b. $152.02; $140.97

31. No; see students' work.

32. pay the customer $27.50

33. 133%

34. 7,500,000 users

35. 8.6%

36. $307.80

37. an increase of more than 22%

38a. no difference

38b. See students' work.

39. 11% decrease

40. 540 seats

41. 65 ft

42. at least 25 feet long

43. 11

44. 101°

45. heavy, 571 Calories; light, 286 Calories

46. scale: from 4 to 10, intervals of 0.2

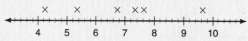

4–6 Integration: Probability   Probability and Odds
Pages 230–232

1. 0

2. 7; a natural number less than 7

3. 5:3

4. See students' work.

5. See students' work.

6. 1

7. $\frac{1}{2}$

8. $\frac{1}{6}$

9. $\frac{2}{3}$

10. 2:1

11. 5:1

12. 4:3

13. $\frac{1}{2}$

14. 1

15. $\frac{1}{2}$

16. 0

17. $\frac{1}{2}$

18. $\frac{1}{12}$

19. $\frac{2}{11}$

20. $\frac{9}{11}$

21. 0

22. $\frac{4}{11}$

23. $\frac{8}{11}$

24. $\frac{2}{11}$

25. 1:5

26. 1:2

27. 4:11

28. 2:1

29. 23:7

30. 1:1

31. $\frac{1}{2}$

32. $\frac{1}{13}$

33. 1:3

34. 25:1

35. $\frac{8}{13}$

36. 2:1

37. $\frac{1}{7}$

38. $\frac{6}{19}$

39a. 1:14

39b. $\frac{1}{27}$

41a. $\frac{3}{26}$

41b. $\frac{4}{13}$

41c. 3:23

43. 9°

45. $50

47. $\frac{4}{21}$

40a. $\frac{4}{35}$

40b. $\frac{4}{23}$

42. 3233%

44. $\frac{8}{5}$; 1.6

46. ±42

48a.

Stem	Leaf
1	6 7 7 8 8 8 8 8 9 9 9 9 9 9 9
2	0 0 2 3 4 4 5 5 6 7 7
3	0 2 3 3 5 6
4	5 8
5	5

3 | 5 = 35

48b. 35 people

48c. 39 years

48d. 19 years

48e. teens

49. 75

1. d = distance, r = rate, t = time
2. to organize information and model the situation
3. See students' work.
4. about 6.7 mL
5. 226 dozen chocolate chip; 311 dozen peanut butter
6. 400 mph
7. 11:30 A.M.
8. 270 solid; 210 print
9. 5 quarters
10. 10 pounds
11. 3 hours
12. 9:30 A.M.
13. 2.5 hours
14. 5 adult tickets, 3 student tickets
15. 46 mph
16. 3.2 quarts
17. 67 mph
18. 240 km
19a. 7
20. 3.56
19b. 16
21. Sample answer: How much pure antifreeze must be mixed with a 20% solution to produce 40 quarts of a 28% solution?
22. 12 miles
23. 0
24. 12,000 bats
25. $11,000
26. 58 feet
27. 49
28. −12
29. associative (+)

1. inverse
2. $y = kx$, where $k \neq 0$
3. Divide each side of $y = kx$ by x.
4. No, because growth rates vary widely.
5. I, 5
6. D, −3
7. 10
8. 10
9. 99
10. $\frac{12}{5}$ or 2.4

11. 20 inches from the 8-ounce weight, 16 inches from the 10-ounce weight

12. D, 3.14

13. I, 15

14. I, 35

15. I, 9

16. D, $\frac{1}{3}$

17. D, 4

18. $2\frac{1}{4}$

19. $26\frac{1}{4}$

20. 100

21. -8

22. -4

23. 12

24. 12

25. 6.075

26. -48

27. 8.3875

28. $\frac{2}{3}$

29. $\frac{1}{4}$

30a. It is halved.

30b. It is divided by 3.

31. 18 pounds

32. 165 pounds

33. 1.6 feet

34. 12:00 noon

35. 2:1

36. $63.20

37. $4300 at 5%, $7400 at 7%

38. 8

39. -12

40. $a + 8$

1. See coordinate plane on page 254.

2. (+, +), I; (−, +), II; (−, −), III; (+, −), IV

3. See students' work.

4. (5, 2); I

5. (−3, −1); III

6. (−2, 3); II

7. (0, −2); none

8–11.
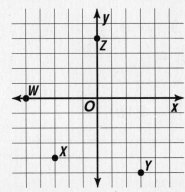

13. (−1, −3); III

15. (0, 3); none

17. (0, 0); none

19. (3, −2); IV

21. (2, 2); I

23. (−5, 4); II

12. (−13, 15)

14. (−2, 0); none

16. (−4, 5); II

18. (5, −5); IV

20. (2, 5); I

22. (4, 4); I

24. (−2, −5); III

25–36.
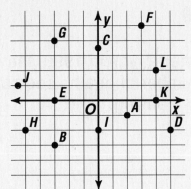

37. M
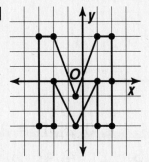

38. airplane
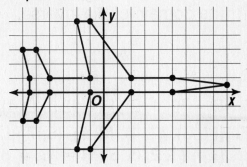

39. See students' work.

40a. I or III

40b. II or IV

40c. x- or y-axis

41a. New Orleans

41b. Oregon

41c. Sample answer: (75°, 40°)

42a. John Kennedy

42b. (1, O)

42c. I-95

41d. Honolulu, Hawaii

41e. See students' work.

41f. Sample answer: The longitude lines are not the same distance apart; they meet at the poles.

43a–b. See students' work.

45. $3\frac{1}{2}$ hours

47. 4; 3; none

49. $-a - 5$

51. $31a + 21b$

42d. (1, P), (1, O), (1, N), (1, M), (1, L), (2, L), (3, L)

44. -5

46. $16°$

48. $\frac{4}{5}$

50a. $65°$

50b. $51°$ to $72°$

5–2 Relations
Pages 266–269

1. The domain values are the *x* values and the range values are the *y* values. If you do not know which is which, your plots will be incorrect.

2. After a high in 1990, the number of deaths seems to be decreasing.

3. The domain of the relation becomes the range of the inverse. The range becomes the domain of the inverse.

4.

5. D = {0, 1, 2}; R = {2, −2, 4}

6. D = {−4, −2, 0, 2}; R = 2, 0, 4}

7. {(1, 3), (2, 4), (3, 5), (5, 7)}; D = {1, 2, 3, 5}; R = {3, 4, 5, 7}; Inv = {(3, 1), (4, 2), (5, 3), (7, 5)}

8. {(1, 4), (3, −2), (4, 4), (6, −2)}; D = {1, 3, 4, 6}; R = {−2, 4}; Inv = {(4, 1), (−2, 3), (4, 4), (−2, 6)}

9. {(1, 3), (2, 2), (4, 9), (6, 5)}; D = {1, 2, 4, 6}; R = {2, 3, 5, 9}; Inv = {(3, 1), (2, 2), (9, 4), (5, 6)}

10. {(−3, −2), (−2, −1), (0, 0), (1, 1)}; D = {−3, −2, 0, 1}; R = {−2, −1, 0, 1}; Inv = {(−2, −3), (−1, −2), (0, 0), (1, 1)}

11. {(−2, 2), (−1, 1), (0, 1), (1, 1), (1, −1), (2, −1), (3, 1)}; D = {−2, −1, 0, 1, 2, 3}; R = {−1, 1, 2}; Inv = {(2, −2), (1, −1), (1, 0), (1, 1), (−1, 1), (−1, 2), (1, 3)}

12.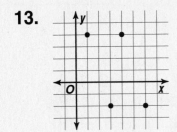

13.

14.

15a. See students' work.

15b. 5.6%

15c. Except for the first 6 months of 1992, the unemployment rate seems to be decreasing.

16. D = {1, 2, 3}; R = {−7, 3, 5, 9}

17. D = {−5, −2, 1, 3}; R = {7}

18. D = {−9, −4.7, 2.4, 3.1}; R = {−3.6, −1, 2, 3.9}

19. D = $\left\{-5\frac{1}{4}, -3, \frac{1}{2}, 1\frac{1}{2}\right\}$;

R = $\left\{-6\frac{2}{7}, -\frac{2}{3}, \frac{1}{4}, \frac{2}{5}\right\}$

20. {(0, 4), (1, 5), (2, 6), (3, 6)}; D = {0, 1, 2, 3}; R = {4, 5, 6}; Inv = {(4, 0), (5, 1), (6, 2), (6, 3)}

21. {(6, 4), (4, −2), (3, 4), (1, −2)}; D = {1, 3, 4, 6}; R = {−2, 4}; Inv = {(4, 6), (−2, 4), (4, 3), (−2, 1)}

22. {(−4, 2), (−2, 0), (0, 2), (2, 4)}; D = {−4, −2, 0, 2}; R = {0, 2, 4}; Inv = {(2, −4), (0, −2), (2, 0), (4, 2)}

23. {(6, 0), (−3, 5), (2, −2), (−3, 3)}; D = {−3, 2, 6}; R = {−2, 0, 3, 5}; Inv = {(0, 6), (5, −3), (−2, 2), (3, −3)}

24. {(5, 2), (−3, 1), (2, 2), (1, 7)}; D = {−3, 1, 2, 5}; R = {1, 2, 7}; Inv = {(2, 5), (1, −3), (2, 2), (7, 1)}

25. {(3, 4), (3, 2), (2, 9), (5, 4), (5, 8), (−7, 2)}; D = {−7, 2, 3, 5}; R = {2, 4, 8, 9}; Inv = {(4, 3), (2, 3), (9, 2), (4, 5), (8, 5), (2, −7)

26. {(0, 100), (5, 90), (10, 81), (15, 73), (20, 66), (25, 60), (30, 55)}; D = {0, 5, 10, 15, 20, 25, 30}; R = {55, 60, 66, 73, 81, 90, 100}; Inv = {(100, 0), (90, 5), (81, 10), (73, 15), (66, 20), (60, 25), (55, 30)}

27. {(0, 25), (1, 50), (2, 75), (3, 100)}; D = {0, 1, 2, 3}; R = (25, 50, 75, 100}; Inv = {(25, 0),(50, 1), (75, 2), (100, 3)}

28. {(1.25, 68.75), (3.75, 206.25), (4.5, 247.5), (5.5, 302.5), (6, 330)}; D = {1.25, 3.75, 4.5, 5.5, 6}; R = {68.75, 206.25, 247.5, 302.5, 330}; Inv = {(68.75, 1.25), (206.25, 3.75), (247.5, 4.5), (302.5, 5.5), (330, 6)}

29. {(−3, 4), (−2, 2), (−1, −2), (2, 2)}; D = {−3, −2, −1, 2}; R = {−2, 2, 4}; Inv = {(4, −3), (2, −2), (−2, −1), (2, 2)}

30. {(−3, 3), (2, 4), (3, 1), (3, −3), (1, −3), (−2, −3)}; D = {−3, −2, 1, 2, 3}; R = {−3, 1, 3, 4}; Inv = {(3, −3), (4, 2), (1, 3), (−3, 3), (−3, 1), (−3, −2)}

31. {(−3, 3), (−3, −3), (3, 3), (3, −3), (0, 0)}; D = {−3, 0, 3}; R = {−3, 0, 3}; Inv = {(3, −3), (−3, −3), (3, 3), (−3, 3), (0, 0)}

32. {(−3, −2), (−2, −1), (−1, 0), (1, 2), (2, 3), (3, 4)}; D = {−3, −2, −1, 1, 2, 3}; R = {−2, −1, 0, 2, 3, 4}; Inv = {(−2, −3), (−1, −2), (0, −1), (2, 1), (3, 2), (4, 3)}

33. {(−3, 1), (−1, 1), (2, 1), (3, 1), (4, 1)}; D = {−3, −1, 2, 3, 4}; R = {1}; Inv = {(1, −3), (1, −1), (1, 2), (1, 3), (1, 4)}

34. {(−2, 4), (−2, 2), (−2, 0), (2, 0), (2, −2), (2, −4)}; D = {−2, 2}; R = {−4, −2, 0, 2, 4}; Inv = {(4, −2), (2, −2), (0, −2), (0, 2), (−2, 2), (−4, 2)}

35.

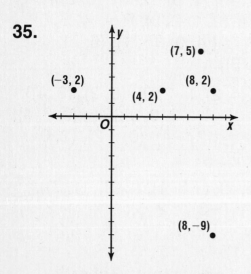

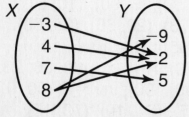

36.

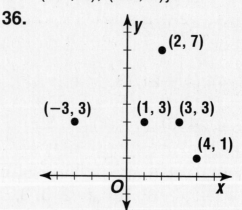

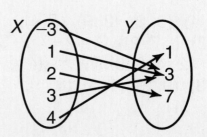

37.

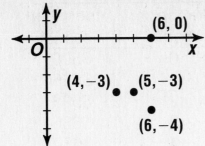

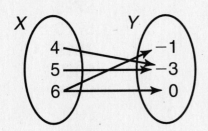

38–40. Windows and graphs may vary. Sample answers are given. See students' graphs.

38a. [1991, 1996] by [0, 900]

38b. {(77, 1992), (200, 1993), (550, 1994), (880, 1995)}

38c. All points lie in Quadrant I.

39a. [−10, 10] by [−10, 10]

39b. {(10, 0), (−8, 3), (6, 6), (−4, 9)}

40a. [−8, 4] by [−4, 36]

40b. {(18, −1), (23, −2), (28, −3), (33, −4)}

39c.

(x, y)	Quadrant	Inverse's Quadrant
(0, 10)	I	I
(3, −8)	IV	II
(6, 6)	I	I
(9, −4)	IV	II

40c.

(x, y)	Quadrant	Inverse's Quadrant
(−1, 18)	II	IV
(−2, 23)	II	IV
(−3, 28)	II	IV
(−4, 33)	II	IV

41. If a point lies in Quadrants I or III, its inverse will lie in the same quadrant as the point. If a point lies in Quadrant II, its inverse lies in Quadrant IV, and vice versa. If a point lies on the x-axis, its inverse lies on the y-axis and vice versa.

42. Relations will vary. Sample answer: {(5, 3), (3, 5), (2, 2), (−4, −2), (−2, −4)}; the graphs are the same.

43a. Sample answer: 157 billion, 191 billion

43b. Sample answer: Retail sales have increased from 1992 to 1994.

43c. Sample answer: As unemployment decreases, retail sales increase because people have more money to spend.

45a.

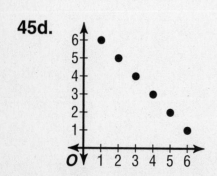

D = R = {1, 2, 3, 4, 5, 6}

45b. D = R = {1, 2, 3, 4, 5, 6}; relation = inverse

45c. 11 possible sums

```
                ×
              × × ×
          × × × × ×
        × × × × × × ×
      × × × × × × × × ×
    × × × × × × × × × × ×
  1  2  3  4  5  6  7  8  9 10 11 12 13
```

45d.

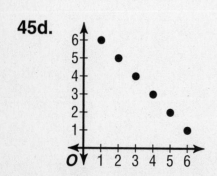

44a.

Number of Weeks	Amount in Account
0	$500
1	$545
2	$590
3	$635
4	$680
5	$725
6	$770
7	$815
8	$860
9	$905
10	$950
11	$995
12	$1040
13	$1085
14	$1130
15	$1175
16	$1220

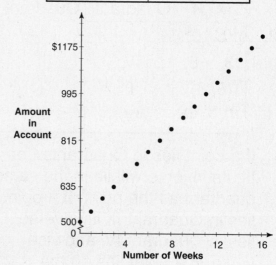

44b. after 16 weeks

46.

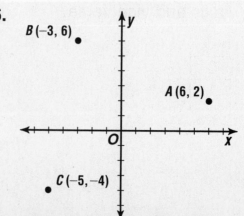

45e. $\frac{6}{36}$; There are 6 out of 36 ways to roll a sum of seven.

47. 32

49. $480

51. 2214, 2290

53. $4 + 80x + 32y$

48. 4 adult, 12 children

50. $m = \dfrac{E}{c^2}$

52a. 27°F

52b. It continually decreases.

5–3 Equations as Relations
Pages 274–277

1a. air, gasoline; air, aluminum, gasoline, lead, silver, steel, water

1b. D = {10, 50, 100, 150}; R = {193, 965, 1930, 2895}

3. A, C, F, G

5. It makes calculating the y value easier.

2. not; $1 + 2(-1) \neq 3$

4. Length of a side cannot be zero or a negative number.

6. The independent variable's values are chosen or assigned. The dependent variable's value varies with the value of the independent variable. The independent variable is graphed along the horizontal axis and the dependent variable along the vertical axis.

7.

x	y	(x, y)
−2	−1	(−2, −1)
−1	1	(−1, 1)
0	3	(0, 3)
1	5	(1, 5)
2	7	(2, 7)
3	9	(3, 9)

8.

b	a	(b, a)
−5	−10	(−5, −10)
−2	$-\frac{11}{2}$	$(-2, -\frac{11}{2})$
0	$-\frac{5}{2}$	$(0, -\frac{5}{2})$
2	$\frac{1}{2}$	$(2, \frac{1}{2})$
5	5	(5, 5)

9. a, d

10. b, c

11. {(−2, 8), (−1, 7.5), (0, 7), (1, 6.5), (2, 6)}

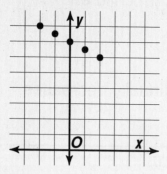

12a. $\ell = \dfrac{A}{w}$ or $\ell = \dfrac{36}{w}$

12b. Sample answer: (1, 36), (2, 18), (3, 12), (4, 9), (6, 6)

13. a, c

14. b, c

15. a, b

16. c, d

17. c

18. a, b, c, d

19. {(−3, −12), (−2, −8), (0, 0), (3, 12), (6, 24)}

20. {(−3, −10), (−2, −7), (0, −1), (3, 8), (6, 17)}

21. {(−3, 10), (−2, 9), (0, 7), (3, 4), (6, 1)}

22. {(−3, −7), (−2, −6), (0, −4), (3, −1), (6, 2)}

23. {(−3, 11), (−2, 9.5), (0, 6.5), (3, 2), (6, −2.5)}

24. {(−3, 19), (−2, 14), (0, 4), (3, −11), (6, −26)}

25. {(−3, −12), (−2, −7), (0, 3), (3, 18), (6, 33)}

26. {(−3, −5.5), (−2, −5), (0, −4), (3, −2.5), (6, −1)}

27. {(−3, 1.8), (−2, 1.4), (0, 0.6), (3, −0.6), (6, −1.8)}

28.

(x, y)
(−3, −9)
(−2, −6)
(−1, −3)
(0, 0)
(1, 3)
(2, 6)
(3, 9)

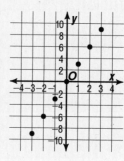

29.

(x, y)
(−5, −9)
(−3, −5)
(0, 1)
(1, 3)
(3, 7)
(6, 13)

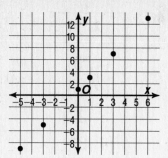

30.

(x, y)
(−3, −7)
(−1, −4)
(2, 0.5)
(4, 3.5)
(7, 8)

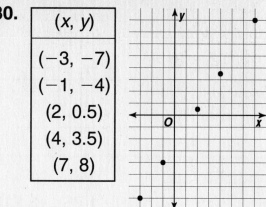

31.

(x, y)
(−2, 4.5)
(−1, 3.25)
(0, 2)
(1, 0.75)
(3, −1.75)
(4, 3)
(5, −4.25)

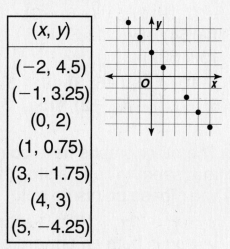

32a. $5a + 5b = 540$

32b. $a = 108 - b$

32c. Sample answer: (1, 107), (2, 106), (3, 105), (4, 104), (5, 103)

33a. $3x + 4y = 180$

33b. $y = 45 - \frac{3}{4}x$

33c. Sample answer: (1, 44.25), (2, 43.5), (3, 42.75), (4, 42), (5, 41.25)

34. $\{-9, -8, -7, -5, -4\}$

35. $\left\{-\frac{2}{3}, -\frac{1}{3}, 0, \frac{2}{3}, 1\right\}$

36. $\left\{-\frac{5}{6}, -\frac{2}{3}, -\frac{1}{2}, -\frac{1}{6}, 0\right\}$

37. $\left\{-\frac{7}{4}, -\frac{1}{2}, 2, \frac{13}{4}, \frac{9}{2}\right\}$

38.

(x, y)
(−3, 8)
(−1, −6)
(0, −10)
(1, −12)
(3, −10)
(5, 0)

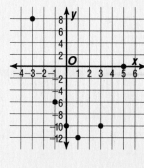

Algebra 1

39.

(x, y)
(−2, −8)
(−1, −1)
(0, 0)
(1, 1)
(2, 8)

40.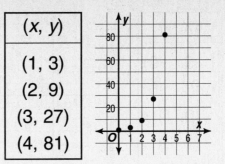

(x, y)
(1, 3)
(2, 9)
(3, 27)
(4, 81)

41. {(−2.5, −4.26), (−1.75, −3.21), (0, −0.76), (1.25, 0.99), (3.33, 3.902)}

42. {(−125, −425.5), (−37, −117.5), (−6, −9), (12, 54), (57, 211.5), (150, 537)}

43. {(−100, 350), (−30, 116.$\overline{6}$), (0, 16.$\overline{6}$), (120, −383.$\overline{3}$), (360, −1183.$\overline{3}$), (720, −2383.$\overline{3}$)}

44. {(−10, 4.$\overline{6}$), (−5, 3), (0, 1.$\overline{3}$), (5, −0.$\overline{3}$), (10, −2), (15, −3.$\overline{6}$)}

45a. {−6, −4, 0, 4, 6}

45b. {−13, −8, −4, 4, 8, 13}

45c. {−5, 0, 4, 8, 13}

46a. The other graphs have points that seem to lie in a straight line. These points do not.

46b. $y = x^2 − 3x − 10$ is U-shaped; $y = x^3$ is both an upward and downward curve; $y = 3^x$ is J-shaped.

47a. $D = \dfrac{m}{V}$

47b. silver and gasoline

48a. $D : R > 0; R : T > 0$

48b. North America, 19; South America, 33; Europe, 54; Asia, 7; Africa, 5

48c. 354,234,275; 504,531,323; 718,597,477

49.

Women		
L	S	(L, S)
$9\frac{1}{3}$	6	$\left(9\frac{1}{3}, 6\right)$
$9\frac{5}{6}$	$7\frac{1}{2}$	$\left(9\frac{5}{6}, 7\frac{1}{2}\right)$
$10\frac{1}{6}$	$8\frac{1}{2}$	$\left(10\frac{1}{6}, 8\frac{1}{2}\right)$
$10\frac{2}{3}$	10	$\left(10\frac{2}{3}, 10\right)$

Men		
L	S	(L, S)
$11\frac{1}{3}$	8	$\left(11\frac{1}{3}, 8\right)$
$11\frac{5}{6}$	$9\frac{1}{2}$	$\left(11\frac{5}{6}, 9\frac{1}{2}\right)$
$12\frac{1}{3}$	11	$\left(12\frac{1}{3}, 11\right)$
$12\frac{5}{6}$	$12\frac{1}{2}$	$\left(12\frac{5}{6}, 12\frac{1}{2}\right)$

50a.

Day	Plan A	Plan B
1	$1	$0.01
2	$2	$0.02
3	$3	$0.04
4	$4	$0.08
5	$5	$0.16
6	$6	$0.32
7	$7	$0.64
8	$8	$1.28
9	$9	$2.56
10	$10	$5.12
11	$11	$10.24
12	$12	$20.48
13	$13	$40.96
14	$14	$81.92
15	$15	$163.84
16	$16	$327.68
17	$17	$655.36
18	$18	$1310.72
19	$19	$2621.44
20	$20	$5242.88
21	$21	$10,485.76
22	$22	$20,971.52
23	$23	$41,943.04
24	$24	$83,886.08
25	$25	$167,772.16
26	$26	$335,544.32
27	$27	$671,088.64
28	$28	$1,342,177.28
29	$29	$2,684,354.56
30	$30	$5,368,709.12

51a.

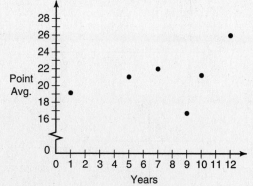

51b. The more years played, the higher the point-per-game average of the player.

50b. On day 12, Plan B exceeds Plan A.

52. star

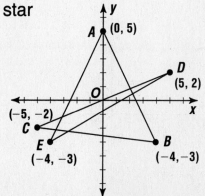

53. $467.50

54. 70

55. $18,000

56. $a = -27c + 6b$

57a. $2w + 2\ell = 148$

58. Sample answer: 0

57b. w, 14.25 in.; ℓ, 59.75 in.

59. -7.976

5–4 Graphing Linear Equations
Pages 283–286

1. Because $3 = -2(-1) + 1$ is a true sentence.

2a. horizontal line

2b. vertical line

2c. slanted line

3. The first graph is a set of points; the second is a line.

4. Time and Calories are nonnegative quantities.

5. See students' work.

6. yes; $3x - 5y = 0$

7. yes; $2x + y = 6$

8. no

9. yes; $3x + 2y = 7$

10.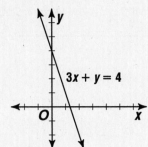

$3x + y = 4$

11.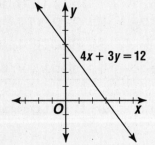

$4x + 3y = 12$

12.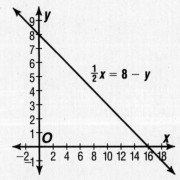

$\frac{1}{2}x = 8 - y$

13.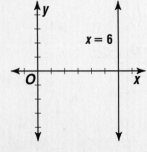

$x = 6$

14.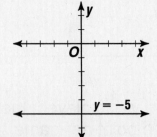

$y = -5$

15.

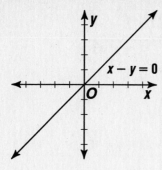

$x - y = 0$

16. no

17. yes; $\frac{3}{5}x - \frac{2}{3}y = 5$

18. no

19. no

20. yes, $3y = -2$

21. yes; $3x - 2y = 8$

22. yes, $5x = 7$

23. yes; $7x - 7y = 0$

24. no

25. yes; $3m - 2n = 0$

26. yes; $\frac{1}{2}x - \frac{2}{3}y = 10$

27. yes; $6a - 7b = -5$

28.

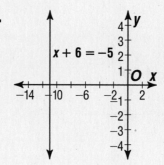

$x + 6 = -5$

29.

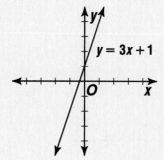

$y = 3x + 1$

30.

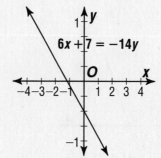

$6x + 7 = -14y$

31.

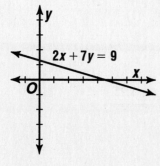

$2x + 7y = 9$

32.

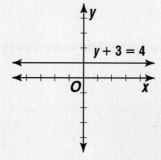

$y + 3 = 4$

33.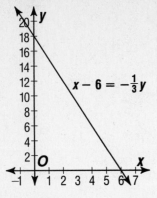

$x - 6 = -\frac{1}{3}y$

34.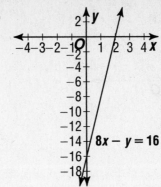

$8x - y = 16$

35.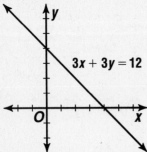

$3x + 3y = 12$

36.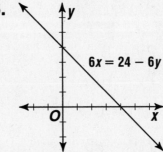

$6x = 24 - 6y$

37.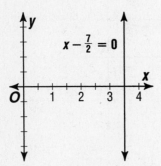

$x - \frac{7}{2} = 0$

38.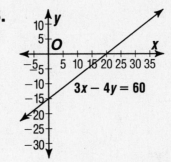

$3x - 4y = 60$

39.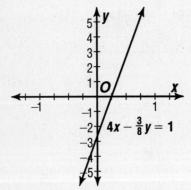

$4x - \frac{3}{8}y = 1$

40.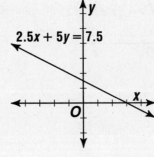

$2.5x + 5y = 7.5$

41.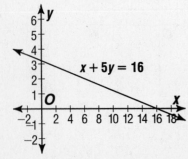

$x + 5y = 16$

42.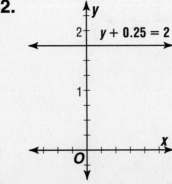

$y + 0.25 = 2$

Algebra 1

43.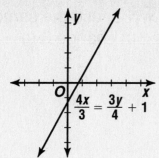
$$\frac{4x}{3} = \frac{3y}{4} + 1$$

44.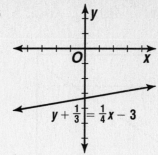
$$y + \frac{1}{3} = \frac{1}{4}x - 3$$

45.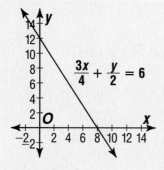
$$\frac{3x}{4} + \frac{y}{2} = 6$$

47. −5, 7.5

49. 6, 9, 10

46. 4, 9

48. 18, 24, 30

50. [−10, 10] by [−10, 10]; Xscl: 1, Yscl: 1

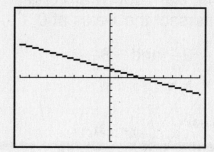

51. [−5, 15] by [−10, 10], Xscl: 1, Yscl: 1

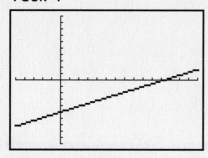

52. [−10, 10] by [−10, 10]; Xscl: 1, Yscl: 1

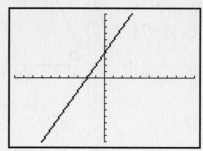

53. [−10, 10] by [−2, 2], Xscl: 1, Yscl: 0.25

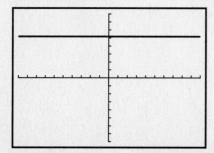

54. [−5, 50] by [−1.5, 0.5]; Xscl: 5, Yscl: 0.25

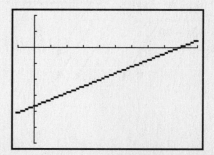

55. [−5, 25] by [−20, 5], Xscl: 5,
Yscl: 5

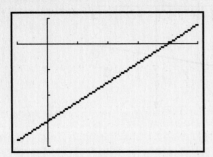

56. Graph of $x = 3$; use the same
procedure but change 3 to −25.

57a. Sample answer: Parallel lines
that slant upward and intersect
the x-axis at −7, −2.5, 0, and
4.5.

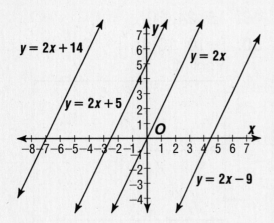

57b. Sample answer: Parallel lines
that slant downward and
intersect the x-axis at 0,

$1\frac{1}{3}$, $2\frac{1}{3}$, and $-3\frac{1}{3}$.

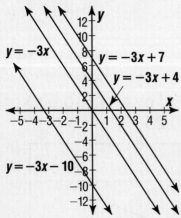

58a. $D : t \geq 0; R : y \geq 0$

58b.

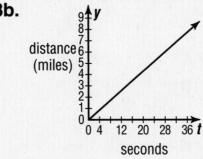

58c. about 14 seconds

Algebra 1

59a.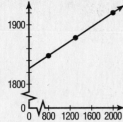

59b. yes, but only if her sales are $1300 or $2000 over target

61. $y = 3 - 4x$

60a. $C = 0.092(68.2)t$

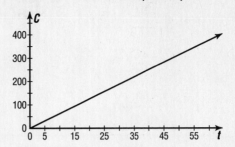

60b. He will burn more Calories in the new routine because $0.092(30)(72.3) + 0.132(30)(72.3) > 0.092(60)(72.3)$.

62.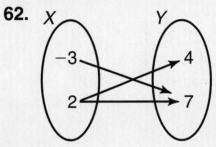

63a.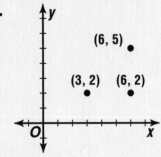

64. $\frac{1}{5}$

63b. (3, 5)

63c. 12 inches

65. 15%

67. 120°

69. $\frac{1}{48}$

66. 15th, 16th, 17th, 18th

68. 6.25 kg

70. 31

1.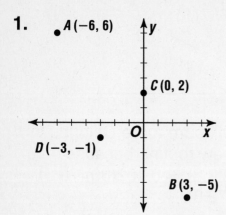

A(−6, 6)

C(0, 2)

D(−3, −1)

B(3, −5)

2. {(1, 3), (2, 7), (4, 1), (−3, 3), (−3, −3)}; D = {−3, 1, 2, 4}; R = {−3, 1, 3, 7}; Inv = {(3, 1), (7, 2), (1, 4), (3, −3), (−3, −3)}

3. {(−5, −3), (−1, 4), (4, 4), (4, −3)}; D = {−5, −1, 4}; R = {−3, 4}; Inv = {(−3, −5), (4, −1), (4, 4), (−3, 4)}

4. $y = 4 - 2x$

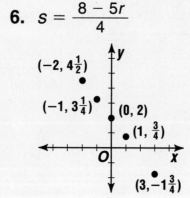

(−2, 8)

(−1, 6)

(0, 4)

(1, 2)

(3, −2)

5. $b = 3 - \frac{2}{3}a$

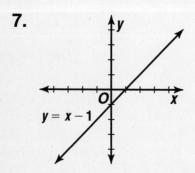

$(-2, 4\frac{1}{3})$

$(-1, 3\frac{2}{3})$

(0, 3)

$(1, 2\frac{1}{3})$

(3, 1)

6. $s = \dfrac{8 - 5r}{4}$

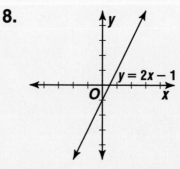

$(-2, 4\frac{1}{2})$

$(-1, 3\frac{1}{4})$

(0, 2)

$(1, \frac{3}{4})$

$(3, -1\frac{3}{4})$

7.

$y = x - 1$

8.

$y = 2x - 1$

9.

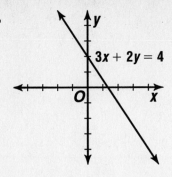

$3x + 2y = 4$

10. about 5.33 m

5–5 Functions
Pages 291–294

1. A relation is a set of ordered pairs. A function is a relation in which each member of the domain is paired with only one member of the range.

2. The value of one variable is dependent upon the value of the other variable. That is, if w is a function of f, the value of w is dependent upon the value of f in the expression defining w.

3. Substitute 1 for x in the equation and evaluate; $g(1) = 15$.

4. False; $x = 4$ is not a function.

5. Sample answer: If you can draw a vertical line through the graph at any point and it intersects the graph more than once, the graph is not the graph of a function.

6. yes

7. no

8. yes

9. yes

10. no

11. yes

12. no

13. no

14. a, c

15. -10

16. 8

17. $3w + 2$

18. $3r - 16$

19. yes

20. no

21. no

22. yes

23. yes

24. no

25. yes

26. no

27. yes

28. yes

29. yes

30. no

31. yes

32. yes

33. no

34. yes

35. -14

36. 8

37. $-\dfrac{9}{25}$

38. 5

39. 5.25

40. 26.8

41. -18

42. 3.84

43. $9b^2 - 6b$

44. $8y + 2$

45. 3

46. $12w^2 - 12w$

47. $5a^4 - 10a^2$

48. $4c + 14$

49. $24p - 36$

50. $-60w - 30$

51a. Sample answer: $f(x) = x$

51b. Sample answer: $f(x) = x^2$

52. b; Each step represents a minute or any part thereof; function.

53. a; It is a step function using individual points, since you cannot have a fraction of a T-shirt.

54a.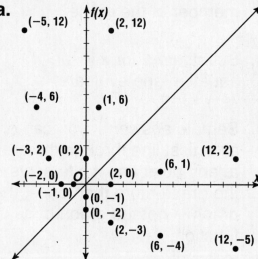

55a. $D : 0 \le k \le 24$;
$R : 0 \le g \le 100$

55b.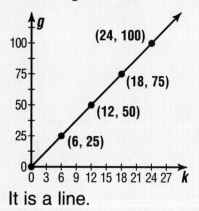
It is a line.

54b. no

54c. The inverse is a reflection of the function with $y = x$ acting as the mirror.

55c. 24 karats

56a. 1125°F

56b. 245°F

56c. Because the crust is thinnest when measured from the bottom of the ocean and thicker from the tops of mountains.

57a. $260.87

57b. Sample equation: $B = \frac{2}{23}P$

58.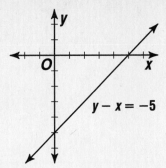

59. $\{-16, -13, 5, 11\}$

60. $\{(1, -1), (9, -5), (6, 4)\}$

61. $\frac{3}{13}$

62. 49.4%

63. 45°

64. 9°

65. -48

66. $115.62

67a.

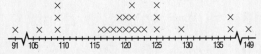

67b. 149

67c. 91

67d. 121 and 125

67e. 13 players

5–6 Writing Equations from Patterns
Pages 298–302

1a. upward
in

2. Test the values of the domain the equation. If the resulting values match the range, the equation is correct.

1b. downward

3. Yes; she can use points on the line since the line represents all solutions to the equation.

4. Sample answer: $2x + y = 3$; No, $4x + 2y = 6$ and other equivalent equations also have these solutions.

5. $f(x) = 2x + 6$

6. $f(x) = \frac{1}{2}x - 5$

7. $y = \frac{1}{2}x - \frac{3}{2}$

8. $y = x$

9. −6

10a.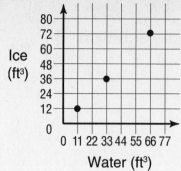

11. 48, 60

12. 0, 1

13. 8, −2

14. 0, 1

15. $f(x) = 5x$

16. $f(n) = 3n - 2$

17. $g(x) = 11 - x$

18. $m(n) = 4n + 5$

19. $h(x) = \frac{1}{3}x - 2$

20. $m(n) = 18 - 2n$

21. $y = -3x$

22. $y = x + 2$

23. $y = \frac{1}{2}x$

24. $y = 6 - x$

25. $y = 2x - 10$

26. $y = 12 - 3x$

27. $xy = -24$

28. $y = x^2 + 1$

29. $y = x^3$

30. $y = \frac{48}{x^2}$

10b. $f(w) = \frac{12}{11}w$

31. y-intercept: $f(0)$, x-intercept: $f(x) = (0)$

32.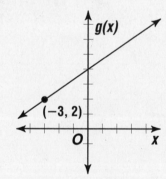

33a. $f(x) = 34x - 34$

33b. You must go deeper in fresh water to get the same pressure as in ocean water.

34a. Sample answer:

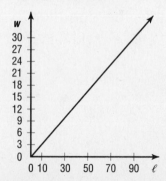

35a. 1514 C

35b. 11.04 C/min

35c.

Minutes	Calories
1	11.04
2	22.08
3	33.12
4	44.16
5	55.2
6	66.24
7	77.28
8	88.32
9	99.36
10	110.4

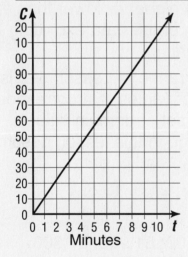

35d. $C(t) = -11.04t$; yes

35e. 1324.8 C burned; yes, 189.2 C remaining

37. D = {1, 3, 5}; R = {2, 4, 6}

39. 5

34b. about 16 lb

34c. $W(\ell) = \frac{23}{70}\ell$

34d. 16.4 lb, slightly more than estimate

36a. 28 times

36b. 10°C

38. 8

40. 43

41.

42.

Stem	Leaf
2	3
3	2
4	3 5 7
5	3 7 8 9 9 9
6	0 0 2 2 4 4 5
•	5 6 6 6 6 6 6
•	6 7 8 8 8 8 9
7	0 2 3 4 4 4 4
•	4 4 4 4 5 5 5
•	5 5 5 5 5 5 5

$$2 \mid 3 = 23¢$$

5–7 Integration: Statistics   Measures of Variation
Pages 309–313

1. San Francisco, 5; Columbus, 35

2. Outliers may make the mean much higher or lower than the mean of the data excluding the outliers.

3a. Sample answer: the basketball teams

3b. Sample answer: the football team

4. The range in Lesson 5–2 is a set of values that correspond to a set of domain values. Range in this lesson describes the spread of data.

5a. See students' work.

5b. See students' work.

6. 13, 17, 21.5, 13.5, 8

7. 45, 40, 45, 34, 11; 11

8. 115,500; 51,900; 57,300; 42,700; 148,000

9. 48, 26, 39, 17, 22

10. Med, 6'2"; Q3, 6'3.5"; Q1, 5'11"; IQR, 4.5"

11. 34, 78, 96, 68, 28

12. 29, 19, 22, 18, 4

13. 10, 5, 8, 2, 6

14. 36, 78.5, 88, 68.5, 19.5

15. 1.1, 30.6, 30.9, 30.05, 0.85

16. 77, 5, 8, 3.2, 4.8

17. 340, 1075, 1125, 1025, 100

18. 4600, 7700, 8600, 6650, 1950

19. 39, 218, 221, 202, 19

20. 4.9, 7.55, 8.4, 6.35, 2.05

21a. 9,198,630; 11,750,000; 5,700,000; 24,000,000; 6,050,000

21b. No; the libraries would have accumulated books throughout the years.

23. 3760, 3224, 4201.5, 2708.5, 1421

25. 21,674; 9790; 12,194; 5475; 6719

27a. males: 36, 29, 37.5, 44, 15; females: 23, 29, 33, 39, 10

27b. There are no outliers.

27c. The ages of the top female golfers are less varied than those of the top male golfers.

29a–c. See students' work.

31. c, d

33a. $6.2 + p = 9.4$; about 3.2 million people

33b. $6.0 + p = 6.9$; about 0.9 million people

22a. Sample answer: {26, 27, 28, 29, 30, 36, 37, 38, 39, 40, 41, 42, 43, 45, 46, 50, 55, 58, 86}

22b. Sample answer: {29, 31, 32, 33, 34, 36, 37, 38, 39, 40, 41, 42, 43, 44, 45, 46, 47, 48, 49}

24. 145,687; 262,306.5; 299,737; 219,683; 80,054

26. 175, 125, 187.5, 92.5, 95

28a. $67.8 million; $50.5 million; $74.1 million; $29.05 million; $45.05 million

28b. There are none.

28c. None of these are on the top 20 list.

30a. $y = 35x + 20$

30b. 475°C

32. 3.75 hours

34. −26

1. From one point to another, go down 3 units and right 5 units. The slope is $-\frac{3}{5}$.

2. It means that as you travel 100 ft horizontally, your altitude increases by 8 ft.

3. Yes, it would affect the sign of the slope.

5. The difference in the x values is always 0, and division by 0 is undefined.

4a.

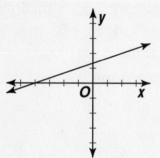

6a.

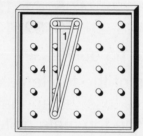

4b.

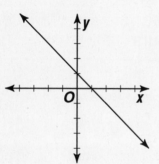

6b.

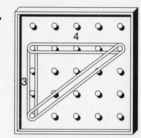

4c.

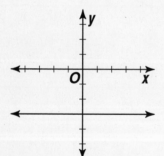

6c.

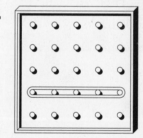

4d.

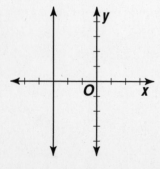

6d.

6e.

7. $\frac{5}{3}$

8. $-\frac{2}{5}$

9. $\frac{3}{2}$

10. $\frac{10}{7}$

11. undefined

12. 7

13. 2

14a. Sample answer: rise, 23 mm; run, 15 mm

14b. based on sample answer, about 1.5

15. $-\frac{1}{5}$

16. $\frac{1}{4}$

17. 0

18. undefined

19. 1

20. -6

21. $\frac{4}{7}$

22. $\frac{3}{8}$

23. $-\frac{2}{3}$

24. 1

25. undefined

26. 0

27. undefined

28. $-\frac{2}{3}$

29. $\frac{9}{5}$

30. 1

31. -5

32. -13

33. -1

34. 7

35. 7

36.

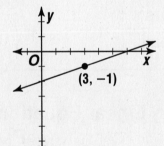

37.

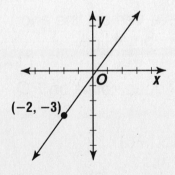

38.

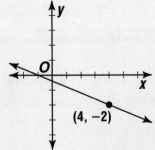

39. Sample answer: (7, 6). The slope of the line containing A and B is -2. Use the slope to go 2 units down and 1 unit to the right of either point.

40. The slope is $\dfrac{120 \text{ in.}}{30 \text{ ft}} = \dfrac{10 \text{ ft}}{30 \text{ ft}}$ or $\dfrac{1}{3}$. Use the slope to figure the length of the support.

distance (in.)	16	32	64	96
length (in.)	$\dfrac{16}{3}$	$\dfrac{32}{3}$	$\dfrac{64}{3}$	$\dfrac{96}{3}$

41. about 1477 feet

43. 11,160 feet

42a. 15 steps

42b. 7.2 in.

44a. 1

44b. $\dfrac{3}{2}$

44c. 1

45. 77; 5; 8; 3.2; 4.8

46. 14, 13

47. 12%

48. $\dfrac{58}{3}$

49. -6

50. 10

51a. 12 animals

52. 14

51b.

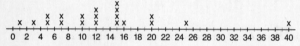

51c. 15 years

51d. 4 animals

6–2 Writing Linear Equations in Point-Slope and Standard Forms
Pages 335–338

1. x_1 and y_1 are the coordinates of a point through which the line passes.

2. $x = 6$ is a vertical line and $y = 6$ is a horizontal line.

3. There would be no variable in the equation.

4. Point R does not lie on $\overleftrightarrow{PQ}$.

5. 4; (2, −3)

6. $-\dfrac{2}{3}$; (−5, −6)

7. 3; (−7, 1)

8. $y - 1 = \dfrac{2}{3}(x - 9)$

9. $y - 4 = -3(x + 2)$

10. $y = 6$

11. $3x + 4y = -9$

12. $5x - 6y = -13$

13. $2x - y = -6$

15. $y + 2 = -\frac{4}{7}(x + 1)$ or $y - 2 =$ $-\frac{4}{7}(x + 8)$; $4x + 7y = -18$

17. $3x - 5y = -2$

19. $y - 5 = 3(x - 4)$

21. $y - 1 = -4(x + 6)$

23. $y - 3 = -2(x - 1)$

25. $y + 3 = \frac{3}{4}(x - 8)$

27. $4x - y = -5$

29. $3x - 2y = -24$

31. $2x + 5y = 26$

33. $y - 2 = -\frac{1}{3}(x + 5)$ or $y + 1 = -\frac{1}{3}(x - 4)$

35. $y + 1 = \frac{3}{7}(x + 8)$ or $y - 5 = \frac{3}{7}(x - 6)$

37. $y + 2 = 0(x - 4)$ or $y + 2 = 0(x - 8)$

39. $4x + 3y = 39$

41. $11x + 8y = 17$

43. $36x - 102y = 61$

45. $\frac{5 - 1}{5 - 9} = \frac{4}{-4}$ or -1
An equation of the line is $(y - 1) = -1(x - 9)$. Let $y = 0$ in the equation and see if $x = 10$.
$$0 - 1 = -x + 9$$
$$-10 = -x$$
$$10 = x \quad \checkmark$$
$(10, 0)$ lies on the line. Since $(10, 0)$ is a point on the x-axis, the line intersects the x-axis at $(10, 0)$.

47a. No, for a rise of 30 inches the ramp must be 30 feet long, but there is only 18 feet available.

14. $y - 1 = -\frac{1}{2}(x + 6)$ or $y - 2 = -\frac{1}{2}(x + 8)$; $x + 2y = -4$

16. $y - 8 = 0$; $y = 8$

18. $y - 8 = 2(x - 3)$

20. $y + 3 = x + 4$

22. $y - 5 = 0$

24. $y - 5 = \frac{2}{3}(x - 3)$

26. $y - 3 = -\frac{2}{3}(x + 6)$

28. $4x - y = -17$

30. $y = -7$

32. $x = -5$

34. $y - 1 = -5(x - 6)$ or $y + 4 = -5(x - 7)$

36. $y - 3 = -\frac{2}{3}(x - 2)$ or $y - 1 = -\frac{2}{3}(x - 5)$

38. $y - 3 = 2.5(x - 2.5)$ or $y + 4.5 = 2.5(x + 0.5)$

40. $3x - y = 1$

42. $4x + y = 1.5$

44. $x = -2$

46a. AC: $y - 4 = \frac{7}{2}(x + 2)$ or $y + 3 = \frac{7}{2}(x + 4)$;
AB: $y - 4 = -\frac{7}{4}(x + 2)$ or $y + 3 = -\frac{7}{4}(x - 2)$;
BC: $y + 3 = 0$

46b. AC: $7x - 2y = -22$;
AB: $7x + 4y = 2$; BC: $y = -3$

48. 9.85%

47b.

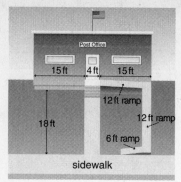

49a. $0.26, $0.09

49b. $0.32

51. 28

53. No; because there could be 2 pink and 1 white or 1 pink and 2 white.

55. associative (=)

50.

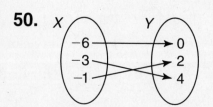

52. 320 mph

54. full; $82.50 vs $96

6–3 Integration: Statistics   Scatter Plots and Best-Fit Lines
Pages 343–345

1. If the slope is positive (or negative), the correlation is positive (or negative).

3a–c. Sample answers are given.

3a. height as you age from 0–12 years

3b. the longer you let water boil to the volume of water in the pan

3c. the height of an adult to their age

4. how strongly the data are correlated; −1 is very negative; 1 is very positive

5. Sample answer: distance driven vs. gallons of gasoline in tank

6. positive

7. positive

8. negative

2. Sample answers are given.

2a.

2b.

2c.

9a. It gets better.

9b. yes; negative

9c. (7, 18) and (8, 16)

10a.

10b. Sample answer: $y = x$

10c. An insect's body temperature closely approximates that of the air around it, and thus, is cold-blooded.

11. positive

12. negative

13. no

14. positive

15. no

16. negative

17. positive

18. positive

19. negative

20. Yes; sample reason: Dots lie in a horizontal pattern.

21. Yes; sample reason: Dots are grouped in an upward diagonal pattern.

22. No; sample reason: Dots are everywhere, no linear pattern exists.

23. c; if 1 is correct then 19 are wrong, If 2 are correct, then 18 are wrong, and so on. Graph c shows these pairs of numbers.

24a.

24b. The points seem to be positively correlated.

24c. $y = 2.48x + 68.94$, $r = 0.501$

24d. Sample answer: As the January temperature increases, so does the July temperature.

25a. Sample answer: The more taxation increases, the more in debt the government becomes.

25b. Sample answer: You work harder and your grades go up.

26. See students' work.

25c. Sample answer: As more money is spent on research, fewer people die of cancer.

25d. Sample answer: comparing the number of professional golfers with the number of holes-in-one

27a. The correlation shown by the graph shows a slightly positive correlation between SAT scores and graduation rate.

27b. See students' graphs. Sample equation: $y = 0.89x + 1142.17$

29a and 29c.

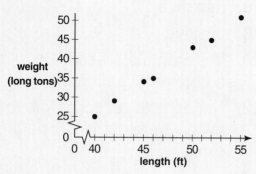

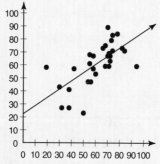

29b. positive

29c. Sample answer: $y = \frac{2}{3}x + 22$

31a. $7500x - y = 120{,}000$

31b. 15,000 feet

31c. No, it only describes the plane's path in that part of the flight.

33. 75°

35. 1.45

28a. There seems to be a positive correlation between the length and weight of humpback whales.

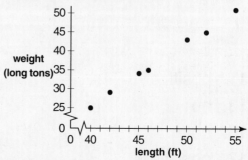

28b. about 43-45 long tons

28c. 43-46 feet

28d. Yes; sample answer: the point (46, 36) falls in the same general area as the other data.

30a–c. See students' work.

32. $\left\{(-2, 5), \left(-1, 5\frac{1}{6}\right), \left(0, 5\frac{1}{3}\right), \left(2, 5\frac{2}{3}\right), \left(5, 6\frac{1}{6}\right)\right\}$

34. $5.1x - 7.6y$

6–4 Writing Linear Equations in Slope-Intercept Form
Pages 349–353

1. Let $x = 0$ to find the y-intercept; let $y = 0$ to find the x-intercept; x: $\frac{C}{A}$; y: $\frac{C}{B}$.

2. Sample answer: Direct variation is the slope-intercept form when $b = 0$.

3. Direct variation may be solved by using the formulas $y = kx$ or $\frac{y}{x} = k$, where $k = m$, which represents the slope.

4. Because its slope is undefined.

5. Both; Chuma's equation is the standard form of Taka's slope-intercept form.

6. Sample answer:
   (1) Use the y-intercept (3) and slope, $-\frac{2}{5}$.
   $$y = mx + b$$
   $$y = -\frac{2}{5}x + 3$$
   (2) Use a point (5, 2) and the slope, $-\frac{2}{5}$.
   $$y - y_1 = m(x - x_1)$$
   $$y - 2 = -\frac{2}{5}(x - 5)$$
   (3) Use two points (1, −3) and (4, 6).
   $$m = \frac{6 - (-3)}{4 - 1} \text{ or } 3$$
   $$y - (-3) = 3(x - 1)$$
   $$y + 3 = 3x - 3$$
   $$y = 3x - 6$$

7a. 2

7b. 2, −4

7c. $y = 2x - 4$

8. 8, 6

9. $-\frac{28}{3}, \frac{7}{2}$

10. $y = -4x + 5$, $4x + y = 5$

11. $y = \frac{2}{3}x - 10$, $2x - 3y = 30$

12. −3, 7

13. −2, −4

14. $\frac{1}{3}, \frac{2}{3}$

15. $x + 5y = 13$

16. $x + 2y = 19$

17. $y = \frac{11}{3}x$; 44

18a. $y = \frac{1}{4}x + 12$

18b. 13.5 feet

19. $-\dfrac{3}{2}$; 0, 0; $y = -\dfrac{3}{2}x$

20. -3; 3, 9; $y = -3x + 9$

21. $\dfrac{2}{5}$; 5, -2; $y = \dfrac{2}{5}x - 2$

22. $-\dfrac{12}{5}$, 4

23. 2, $\dfrac{8}{7}$

24. -1, $\dfrac{2}{5}$

25. $-\dfrac{5}{6}$, 5

26. -3, $\dfrac{3}{4}$

27. none, 6

28. $y = 3x + 5$, $3x - y = -5$

29. $y = 7x - 2$, $7x - y = 2$

30. $y = -6x$, $6x + y = 0$

31. $y = -1.5x + 3.75$, $6x + 4y = 15$

32. $y = \dfrac{1}{4}x - 10$, $x - 4y = 40$

33. $y = -7$, $y = -7$

34. $\dfrac{2}{3}$, -3

35. $-\dfrac{5}{4}$, $\dfrac{5}{2}$

36. 12, 6

37. -4, 12

38. $\dfrac{1}{5}$, $-\dfrac{2}{5}$

39. $\dfrac{4}{5}$, $\dfrac{4}{15}$

40. $10x - 7y = 5$

41. $y = -2$

42. $3x + 10y = -8$

43. $x = 3$

44. $5x + 12y = 83$

45. $y = 9$

46. $y = -\dfrac{8}{5}x$, $-\dfrac{55}{8}$

47. $y = \dfrac{11}{24}x$, $\dfrac{33}{2}$

48. $y = -\dfrac{3}{17}x$, -85

49. $y = \dfrac{2}{3}x - \dfrac{8}{3}$

50. $\left(-\dfrac{5}{2}, -\dfrac{15}{2}\right)$

51. $(-3, -1)$

52. $2x - 7y = 14$

53a. $y = 2.04x - 21.32$

54. $y = -\dfrac{qx}{p} + q$

55a. 42.24 ft³

55b. 270 K

56a. Sample answer:
$y = 0.20x - 326.8$

56b. Sample answer:
$y = 0.18x - 279.8$

56c–d.

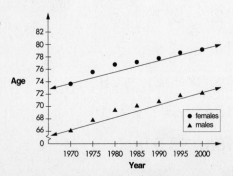

56e. The life expectancy of females is higher than the life expectancy of males and, as time passes, the life expectancy of both increases. According to the graph, at approximately the year 2350, men and women both will have a life expectancy of about 136 years.

56f. based on sample equations: males 93.2; females, 98.2

57a. $y = 0.1x + 3$

57b. Go to the other bank, since this one would charge you $5.50

58a–b.

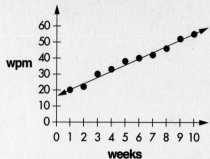

58b. $y = 4x + 17$

58c. about 65 wpm

58d. There's a limit as to how fast one can type.

59. 0

60. $n = 12 - 3m$

61.

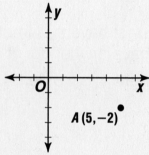

62. $\frac{1}{2}$

63. 13 ft 11 in.

64. $y = 3 - 4x$

65. -9

66. 2

67. $14x + 14$

Self Test
Page 353

1. -1

2. 0

3. undefined

4. 4

5. $y - 4 = \frac{1}{2}(x + 6)$

6. $y - 12 = 0$

7. $x + 5y = 17$

8a–b.

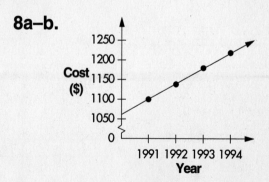

8b. Sample equation:
$y = 40x - 78,537$

8c. positive

8d. Each year the cost of a computer increases.

8e. The number of features on a computer increases more quickly than the cost. Thus, it costs less to buy specific features on a computer now than it did a year ago.

9. $-6, -14$

10. $y = \frac{1}{2}x - 3$

6–5 Graphing Linear Equations
Pages 359–361

1. You can graph a line if you know the slope and a point on the line.

2. A twig cannot have a diameter of 0 and have any length at all.

3. Sample answer: For (2, 3) and $m = \frac{2}{3}$, you graph (2, 3) and move 2 units up and 3 units right to plot the second point. You can repeat the movements to find additional points.

4. down 3, right 4; up 3, left 4.

5. See students' work.

6.

$3x - 8y = 12$

7.

$y + 5 = -2(x + 1)$

8.

$\frac{2}{3}x + \frac{1}{2}y = 3$

9.

$y = 2x - 3$

10.

$y = \frac{2}{5}x - 4$

11.

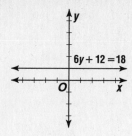

$6y + 12 = 18$

12.

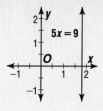

$5x = 9$

13a, d.

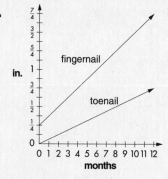

fingernail

in.

toenail

months

14.

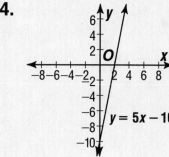

$y = 5x - 10$

13b. $1\frac{3}{4}$ inches

13c. $\frac{1}{16}$ inch

13e. the rate of growth per month

15.

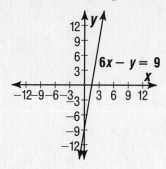

$6x - y = 9$

16.

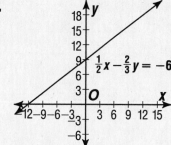

$\frac{1}{2}x - \frac{2}{3}y = -6$

17.

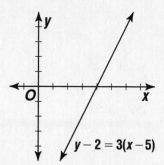

$y - 2 = 3(x - 5)$

18.

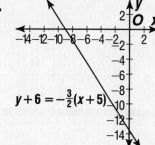

$y + 6 = -\frac{3}{2}(x + 5)$

19.

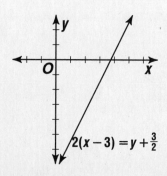

$2(x - 3) = y + \frac{3}{2}$

20.

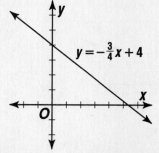

$y = -\frac{3}{4}x + 4$

Algebra 1

21.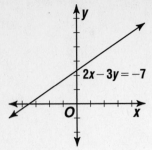

$2x - 3y = -7$

22.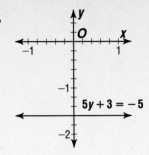

$5y + 3 = -5$

23.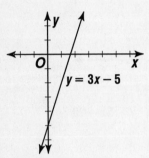

$y = 3x - 5$

24.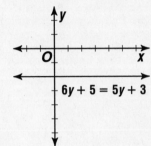

$6y + 5 = 5y + 3$

25.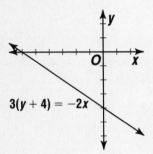

$3(y + 4) = -2x$

26.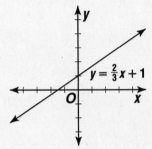

$y = \frac{2}{3}x + 1$

27.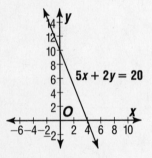

$5x + 2y = 20$

28.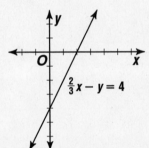

$\frac{2}{3}x - y = 4$

29.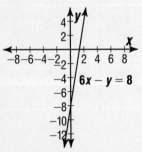

$6x - y = 8$

30.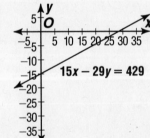

$15x - 29y = 429$

31.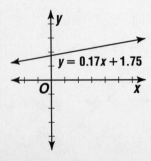

$y = 0.17x + 1.75$

32.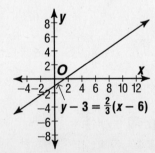

$y - 3 = \frac{2}{3}(x - 6)$

Algebra 1

33.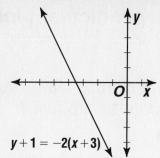

$y + 1 = -2(x + 3)$

34.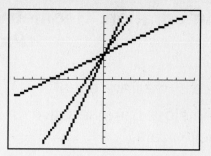

This is a family of graphs in which the slope of each graph is positive and the graphs have the same *y*-intercept.

35.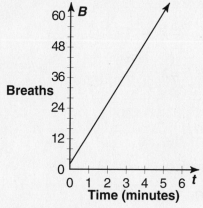

This is a family of graphs in which the slope of the graphs is the same and the graphs are parallel.

36. It has the same slope as $y = 3x$. Graph the intercept and use the slope, 3.

37a.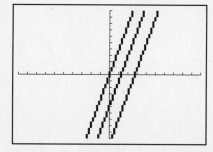

37b. 122 breaths

39. $y = \frac{2}{5}x + 12$

38a.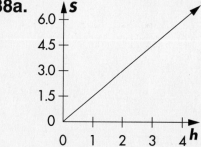

38b. 20 feet

40.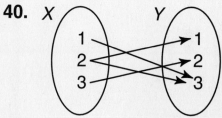

41. 4:30 P.M.

43. 1.8

45. a number *m* minus 1

42. 93°

44. − 22

6–6 Integration: Geometry   Parallel and Perpendicular Lines
Pages 366–368

1a. The slopes are equal.

1b. The slopes are negative reciprocals.

2. Negative reciprocals are two numbers whose product is -1; -2 and $\frac{1}{2}$.

3.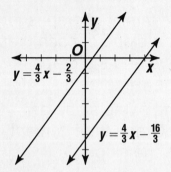

4. If it were not, a and b would be equal.

5a. Slopes are different, relationship is not.

6. $\frac{6}{5}$, $-\frac{5}{6}$

5b. Sample answer: The relationship would not work because there would be no perpendicular lines.

7. $\frac{2}{3}$, $-\frac{3}{2}$

8. $\frac{3}{10}$, $-\frac{10}{3}$

9. perpendicular

10. parallel

11. $y = \frac{5}{6}x - \frac{21}{2}$

12. $y = \frac{5}{2}x + 4$

13. $y = x - 9$

14. $y = \frac{4}{7}x + \frac{3}{7}$

15. $y = \frac{9}{5}x$

16. $y = -\frac{5}{2}x + 2$

17. perpendicular

18. parallel

19. parallel

20. neither

21. perpendicular

22. neither

23. perpendicular

24. $y = x - 9$

25. $y = x + 1$

26. $y = -\frac{2}{3}x - \frac{22}{3}$

27. $y = \frac{8}{7}x + \frac{2}{7}$

28. $y = -2x$

29. $y = 2.5x - 5$

30. $y = \frac{1}{3}x - \frac{17}{3}$

31. $y = \frac{2}{3}x + 4$

32. $y = -0.5x$

33. $y = -\frac{9}{2}x + 14$

34. $y = -3x - 8$

35. $y = 3x - 19$

36. $y = -\frac{5}{3}x + 8$

37. $y = -\frac{1}{5}x - 1$

38. $y = -\frac{3}{5}x + \frac{14}{5}$

39. $y = -\frac{7}{2}x + 11$

40. $y = -\frac{4}{3}x + 11$

41. $y = -3$

42. $x = -5$

43. $y = \frac{5}{4}x$

44. $y = -\frac{3}{5}x + \frac{9}{5}$

45. $y = \frac{1}{3}x - 6$

46a. $y = 2x, \ y = -\frac{1}{2}x + \frac{15}{2}$

46b.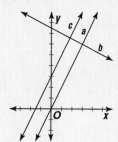

46c. parallel

47. No, because the slope of $\overline{AC}$ is $\frac{6}{7}$ and the slope of $\overline{BD}$ is $-\frac{2}{3}$. These slopes are not negative reciprocals, so the diagonals are not perpendicular.

48a. 10

48b. $y = -\frac{1}{10}x + \frac{39}{10}, \ y = 10x + 14$

49a. $y = \frac{1}{2}x + \frac{7}{2}, \ y = -2x + 11$

49b. right or 90° angle

50.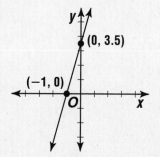

51.

52.

x	−1	2	5	8	11	14
$f(x)$	**5**	−1	−7	**−13**	−19	**−25**

53. $242.80

54. −104

55a. $\frac{5}{12}; \frac{7}{12}$

56. −0.3005

55b. 16-karat gold

57. multiplicative identity

58. 6.28

1a. The x-coordinates will be the same, so calculate the average of the y-coordinates.

1b. The y-coordinates will be the same, so calculate the average of the x-coordinates.

3a–c. See students' work.

5. (1.5, 6)

7. (−6, 1)

9. (−11, 7)

11. (8, 9.8)

13. (12.5, 6)

15. (1, 5)

17. (3, 2)

19. $\left(\frac{1}{2}, 1\right)$

21. (0.8, 2.7)

23. (4x, 9y)

25. (−7, 0)

27. (21, −6)

29. (9, 10)

31. $\left(\frac{5}{6}, \frac{1}{3}\right)$

33. B(2.3, 6.8)

35. P(6.65, −1.85)

37. (−1, 5)

2. C(−6, 9)

4. (5, 3)

6. (10, 6)

8. (−6, 4)

10. (2, 6)

12. (−3, 5)

14. (−1, 6)

16. (9, −3)

18. (−8, 4.3)

20. $\left(\frac{11}{2}, \frac{3}{2}\right)$

22. $\left(\frac{a + c}{2}, \frac{b + d}{2}\right)$

24. $\left(2w, -\frac{5}{2}v\right)$

26. (0, 0)

28. (7, 5)

30. (11, −6)

32. (x, y)

34. A(−2.9, 7.1)

36. B(3.8, 4.5)

38. (8.5, 1)

39. $\left(1, \dfrac{5}{2}\right)$

41a. $N(6, 3)$, $M(10, 3)$

41b. parallel, $MN = \dfrac{1}{2}AB$

43a. $P(-4, 1)$, $Q(10, -1)$

43b. 62 square units; Sample answer: The area of the smaller triangle is $\dfrac{1}{2}bh$. Since the base of the larger triangle is twice that of the smaller one and the height is also twice the length of the smaller one, the area of the larger is $\dfrac{1}{2}(2b)(2h)$, or $2bh$. This is 4 times the area of the smaller one.

45. $y = -\dfrac{7}{9}x - \dfrac{8}{3}$

47. yes; $9x - 6y = 7$

49. -20

51. $3.1x + 1.54$

40. Vertices are $W(2, -3)$, $X(6, 2)$, $Y(2, 4)$, and $Z(-2, -1)$. Slope of $\overline{XW}$ = slope of $\overline{YZ} = \dfrac{5}{4}$. Slope of $\overline{WZ}$ = slope of $\overline{XY} = -\dfrac{1}{2}$. Opposite sides are parallel, so $WXYZ$ is a parallelogram.

42a. $(40, 77)$

42b. $(31, 47)$

42c. Ordered pairs are (y, x) and the origin is in a different place.

44. $y - \dfrac{3}{5}x + \dfrac{14}{5}$

46. $16b^2 - 4b$

48. $38°$

50a. 10 years old

50b. $a + 10$

50c. no; $4 + 10 \neq 12$

Chapter 7   Solving Linear Inequalities
7–1 Solving Inequalities by Using Addition and Subtraction
Pages 387–390

1. Sample answer: $x + 5 < -5$, $x - 5 < -15$, $2x < x - 10$

2. The set of all numbers w such that w is greater than -3.

3. One ($\leq$) includes -7; the other does not.

4. Answers and graphs will vary. Sample answer: The circle on the graph will be filled if the inequality involves $\leq$ or $\geq$. The circle will be open if it involves $>$ or $<$. The arrow goes to the left if it involves $<$ or $\leq$. It goes to the right for $>$ or $\geq$.

5. Yes, sample answer: $x + 6 > x + 8$.

6. See students' work.

7. c

8. a

9. d

10. b

11. $\{x \mid x > -5\}$

12. $\{x \mid x \leq 2\}$

13. $\{y \mid y < -5\}$

14. $\{q \mid q \leq -97\}$

15. $x - 17 < -13$, $\{x \mid x < 4\}$

16. $x + 4 \geq 3$, $\{x \mid x \geq -1\}$

17. $\{a \mid a < 18\}$

13 14 15 16 17 18 19 20 21

18. $\{m \mid m < -14\}$

−19 −18 −17 −16 −15 −14 −13 −12

19. $\{x \mid x \leq 1\}$

−4 −3 −2 −1 0 1 2 3 4

20. $\{d \mid d > 18\}$

13 14 15 16 17 18 19 20 21

21. $\left\{x \mid x > \dfrac{11}{3}\right\}$

1 2 3 $\frac{11}{3}$ 5 6 7 8 9

22. $\{n \mid n \geq -0.15\}$

−3 −2 −0.15 1 2 3 4 5

23. $\{x \mid x > 2\}$

−1 0 1 2 3 4 5 6 7

24. $\{h \mid h \leq 1\}$

−4 −3 −2 −1 0 1 2 3 4

25. $\left\{x \mid x < \dfrac{3}{8}\right\}$

26. $\left\{x \mid x \geq \dfrac{1}{5}\right\}$

27. $\{x \mid x \leq 15\}$

28. $\{w \mid w \geq 0\}$

29. $\{x \mid x < 0.98\}$

30. $\{x \mid x \geq 1\}$

31. $\{r \mid r < 10\}$

32. $\{x \mid x \le -34\}$

33. $x - (-4) \ge 9$, $\{x \mid x \ge 5\}$

34. $x + 5 \ge 17$, $\{x \mid x \ge 12\}$

35. $3x < 2x + 8$, $\{x \mid x < 8\}$

36. $21 \ge x + (-2)$, $\{x \mid x \le 23\}$

37. $20 + x < 3$, $\{x \mid x < 33\}$

38. $4x + 7 < 3x$, $\{x \mid x < -7\}$

39. $2x > x - 6$, $\{x \mid x > -6\}$

40. $100 - x \ge x + 16$, $\{x \mid x \le 42\}$

41. -2

42. 5

43. -2

44. 5

45a. no

45b. yes

45c. yes

45d. yes

46. Answers will vary. Sample answer: $x = 4$, $y = 2$, $t = 3$, $w = 0$

47. The value of x falls between -2.4 and 3.6.

48a. $247 + x \ge 320$

48b. $\{x \mid x \ge 73\}$

70 71 72 73 74 75 76 77 78

49a. $x \le \$12.88$

50. $(-3, 7)$

49b. Sample answer: There may be sales tax on his purchases.

51. $y = -3x + 3$

52. $y = 15x - 3$

53. 42, 131, 145, 159, 28

54. $\left\{(-2, 8), \left(-1, \frac{20}{3}\right), \left(0, \frac{16}{3}\right), \left(2, \frac{8}{3}\right), \left(5, -\frac{4}{3}\right)\right\}$

55. 12

56. $-\dfrac{3}{16}$

57. $<$

58. 120 triangles

Algebra 1

7–2 Solving Inequalities by Using Multiplication and Division
Pages 395–398

1a. False; change $>$ to $<$ in the second inequality.

1b. true

3. Utina is correct because the only time the inequality symbol changes in solving an inequality is when you must multiply or divide by a negative to solve for the variable. For example, in $-3x > 12$, the inequality symbol changes. However, in $3x > -12$, the inequality symbol does not change.

5. $\{x \mid x > -3\}$

7. $\{x \mid x \leq -1.5\}$

2a. negative

2b. $-\dfrac{1}{6}$

2c. $90°$

4. $\{x \mid x < 5\}$

6. $\{x \mid x > -13\}$

8a. $>$

8b. $<$

8c. cannot be determined

9. $\times -\dfrac{1}{6}, \div -6$; yes; $\{y \mid y \leq 4\}$

10. $\times \dfrac{1}{10}, \div 10$; no; $\{x \mid x > 2\}$

11. $\times 4$; no; $\{x \mid x < -20\}$

12. $\times -\dfrac{7}{2}$; yes; $\{z \mid z \leq 42\}$

13. $\{x \mid x < 30\}$

14. $\{v \mid v \leq -12\}$

15. $\{t \mid t \leq -30\}$

16. $\{y \mid y > -5\}$

17. $\dfrac{1}{5}x \leq 4.025$; $\{x \mid x \leq 20.125\}$

18. $-6x < 216$; $\{x \mid x > -36\}$

19. $s \geq 12$

20. $\{a \mid a \leq 7\}$

21. $\{b \mid b > -12\}$

22. $\{w \mid w < 25\}$

23. $\{x \mid x \geq -44\}$

24. $\{x \mid x < -4\}$

25. $\{r \mid r < -6\}$

26. $\{b \mid b \geq -36\}$

27. $\{t \mid t < 169\}$

28. $\{w \mid w > -33\}$

29. $\{g \mid g \geq 7.5\}$

30. $\left\{b \mid b > \dfrac{28}{15}\right\}$

31. $\{x \mid x \geq -0.7\}$

32. $\left\{h \mid h < \dfrac{1}{7}\right\}$

33. $\left\{r \mid r < -\dfrac{1}{20}\right\}$

34. $\left\{b \mid b \leq \dfrac{8}{9}\right\}$

35. $\{x \mid x < -27\}$

36. $\{y \mid y \geq 3\}$

37. $\{m \mid m \geq -24\}$

38. $4x \leq 36; \{x \mid x \leq 9\}$

39. $36 \geq 0.5x; \{x \mid x \leq 72\}$

40. $-3x > 48; \{x \mid x < -16\}$

41. $\frac{3}{4}x \leq -24; \{x \mid x \leq -32\}$

42. $0.80x < 24; \{x \mid x < 30\}$

43. $-8x \leq 144;$ -18 or greater

44. $x \geq 8.5$ feet

45. $y < 7.14$ meters

46. $18m$

47. $\geq$

48. -48

49. $<$

50. Answers will vary. Sample answer: $x = -1, y = -2$

51. up to 416 miles

52. at least 3

53. at least 5883 signatures

54. $5a - 4a + 7 \leq 34; a \leq 27$

55. $(-1, 1)$

56. $-3; \frac{1}{3}$

57. -2

58. $b = a - 3$

59. $155.64

60. 12.69

61. 65 yd by 120 yd

62. 9.5

7–3 Solving Multi-Step Inequalities
Pages 402–404

1. Sample answer:
$$-3x + 7 < 4x - 5$$
$$3x - 3x + 7 < 4x - 5 + 3x$$
$$7 < 7x - 5$$
$$7 + 7 < 7x - 5 + 5$$
$$12 < 7x$$
$$\frac{12}{7} < \frac{7x}{7}$$
$$\frac{12}{7} < x \text{ or } x > \frac{12}{7}$$

2. $4s + 3 \leq 50$

3. Answers will vary. Sample answer: $x + 1 < x - 1$.

4. Add $5w$ to each side. Subtract 29 from each side. Divide each side by 5. The solution is $\left\{w \mid w < -\frac{13}{5}\right\}$.

5. Sample answer: Method 2, because it is shorter.

6a. $x \leq -3$

6b. $x < 2$

7. c

8. b

9. $\{x \mid x > 2\}$

10. $\{h \mid h < -2\}$

11. $\{d \mid d > -125\}$

12. $\{a \mid a < 2\}$

13. $\{2, 3\}$

14. $\{-6, -5, -4, -3\}$

15a. $x + (x + 2) > 75$

16. $\{7, 8, 9, 10\}$

15b. $x > 36.5$

15c. Sample answer: 38 and 40.

17. $\{-10, -9, \ldots, 2, 3\}$

18. $\{-10, -9, -8, \ldots, 8, 9, 10\}$

19. $\{-10, -9, \ldots, -5, -4\}$

20. $\{m \mid m > 5\}$

21. $\{t \mid t > 3\}$

22. $\left\{x \mid x \le -\dfrac{4}{3}\right\}$

23. $\{w \mid w \le 15\}$

24. $\left\{x \mid x < \dfrac{10}{3}\right\}$

25. $\{n \mid n > -9\}$

26. $\{x \mid x > 12\}$

27. $\{m \mid m < 15\}$

28. $\{x \mid x < 19\}$

29. $\{x \mid x < -15\}$

30. $\{r \mid r \le -9\}$

31. $\left\{p \mid p \le \dfrac{14}{3}\right\}$

32. $\{y \mid y < 4\}$

33. $\{x \mid x > -10\}$

34. $\{q \mid q > 4.5\}$

35. $\{k \mid k \le -1\}$

36. $\{h \mid h < -79\}$

37. $\{y \mid y < -1\}$

38. $\dfrac{2}{3}x - 27 \ge 9$; $\{x \mid x \ge 54\}$

39. $3(x + 7) > 5x - 13$; $\{x \mid x < 7\}$

40. $2x + 2 \le 123$; 59 and 61

41. $2x + 2 \le 18$ for $x > 0$; 7 and 9; 5 and 7; 3 and 5; 1 and 3

42. $3x + 6 < 40$; 2, 4, 6; 4, 6, 8; 6, 8, 10; 8, 10, 12; 10, 12, 14

43. no solution $\{\varnothing\}$

44. $\{y \mid y$ is a real number.$\}$

45a. $x \le -8$

45b. $x > 8$

46. the numbers between -5 and 2 or $\{x \mid -5 < x < 2\}$

45c. $x > 2$

45d. $x \le -1$

47. $x + 0.04x + 0.15(x + 0.04x) \le \$50$, $x \le \$41.80$

48. 15 games

49. at least $571,428.57

50. at least $96,774

51a. at most 2.9 weeks

52. $\{r \mid r < -6.6\}$

51b. no change

51c. at most 4.1 weeks

53. $\{y \mid y > 10\}$

54. $y = -\dfrac{1}{2}x + 6$

55. $3x + 2y = 14$

56. 41 cars

57. {−5, −3, −2, 4, 16}   **58.** 1:4
59. 25.1; 23.5; no mode   **60.** 52

7–4 Solving Compound Inequalities
Pages 409–412

1. Answers will vary. Sample answer: The price of an item is at most $18.50 but more than $7.50.

2. $x < -4$ or $x \geq 1$

3. Sample answers: Draw a diagram (helps you to see the solution), make a table (helps you to see a pattern), look for a pattern (determines how the table relates to the number of people seated).

4. The one containing *and* is true when both inequalities are true; the one containing *or* is true if either inequality is true.

5. Helps you plan the solution; provides the solution.

6.

7. $0 \leq x \leq 9$

8. $-2 < x < 3$

9. $-3 < x \leq 1$

10. $x < -2$ or $x > 0$

11. The solution is the empty set. There are no numbers greater than 5 but less than −3.

12. $\{y \mid -4 \leq y < 2\}$

13. $\{h \mid h \leq -7$ or $h \geq 1\}$

14. $\{b \mid b \geq 0\}$

15. $\{w \mid 1 > w \geq -5\}$

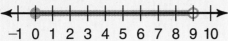

16. $\$0 \leq c \leq \$100$

17. Drawings will vary; 16 pieces.

18.

19. $\varnothing$

20.

21.

22.

23.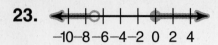
  −10−8−6−4−2 0 2 4

24. $-3 < x < 1$

25. $-4 \le x \le 5$

26. $x < 0$ or $x > 2$

27. $x \le -2$ or $x > 1$

28. $\{m \mid m > 3$ or $m < -1\}$

  −3−2−1 0 1 2 3 4 5

29. $\{x \mid -1 < x < 5\}$

  −3−2−1 0 1 2 3 4 5 6 7

30. $\{y \mid -7 < y < 6\}$

  −12−9−6−3 0 3 6 9 12

31. $\{x \mid x < -2$ or $x > 3\}$

  −4−3−2−1 0 1 2 3 4 5

32. $\{p \mid p < -1\}$

  −7−6−5−4−3−2−1 0 1

33. $\{c \mid c < 7\}$

  1 2 3 4 5 6 7 8 9

34. $\{x \mid 3 < x < 6\}$

  1 2 3 4 5 6 7 8

35. $\varnothing$

36. $\{q \mid -1 < q < 6\}$

  −4−2 0 2 4 6 8 10

37. $\{x \mid x$ is a real number.$\}$

  0 1 2 3 4 5 6 7 8

38. $\{n \mid n \le 4\}$

  −2−1 0 1 2 3 4 5 6

39. $\{y \mid y > 3$ and $y \ne 6\}$

  1 2 3 4 5 6 7 8 9

40. $\left\{z \mid z \ge -\dfrac{2}{3}\right\}$

  −2   −1   0   1

41. $\{x \mid x$ is a real number.$\}$

  −4−3−2−1 0 1 2 3 4

42. $\left\{y \mid y < \dfrac{3}{2}\right\}$

  −1   0   1   2   3

43. $\{w \mid w < 4\}$

  −2−1 0 1 2 3 4 5 6

44. Sample answer: $x > -2$ or $x < 4$

45. Sample answer: $x > 5$ and $x < -4$

46. $50 < 3d + 5 < 89$; $\{d \mid 15 < d < 28\}$

47. $n + 2 \le 6$ or $n + 2 \ge 10$; $\{n \mid n \le 4$ or $n \ge 8\}$

48. $7 < 2n + 5 < 11$; $\{n \mid 1 < n < 3\}$

49. $31 \le 6n - 5 \le 37; \{n \mid 6 \le n \le 7\}$

50. $\{y \mid -1 < y < 3\}$

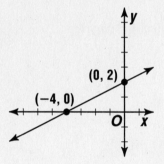

-3 -2 -1 0 1 2 3 4 5

51. $\{m \mid -4 < m < 1\}$

-6 -5 -4 -3 -2 -1 0 1 2 3

52. $\left\{x \mid x < -\dfrac{5}{3} \text{ or } x > 0\right\}$

-2 -1 0

53a. $\{x \mid x < -7 \text{ or } x > 1\}$

53b. $\{x \mid -5 \le x < 1\}$

54. $a \le 0$

55. $-4 \le x \le -1.5 \text{ or } x \ge 2$

56. 1-Darryl, 2-Adrienne, 3-Allison,
4-Mr. Crawford, 5-Don,
6-Benito, 7-Cheri, 8-Belinda

57. $4.4 < x < 6.7$

58. $92 \le s \le 100$

59. $\left\{m \mid m \ge \dfrac{44}{3}\right\}$

60. $\{x \mid x \le -18\}$

61. -5

62. $\dfrac{3}{7}$

63.

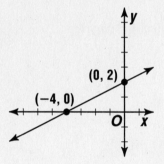

(0, 2)

(−4, 0)

64. $f(x) = -2x + 5$

65. a little more than half a mile

66. $-\dfrac{21}{4}$

67. $18px - 15bg$

68. 63

Self Test
Page 412

1. $\{y \mid y \geq -17\}$

2. $\{r \mid r < -6\}$

3. $\{n \mid n < 4\}$

4. $\{w \mid w < -6.5\}$

5. $\{g \mid g < -5\}$

6. $\{y \mid y \geq 15\}$

7. c

8. $\{t \mid t < -2 \text{ or } t > -1\}$

9. more than 17 points

10a. (2, 1), (2, 3), (2, 5), (4, 1), (4, 3), (4, 5), (6, 1), (6, 3), (6, 5)

10b. 3

7–5 Integration: Probability   Compound Events
Pages 415–419

1.

2. See students' work.

3. A compound event consists of two or more simple events. Tossing a coin is a simple event while tossing two coins is a compound event.

4. Answers may vary. Sample answer: The one in Example 2 involves two events while the one in Example 3 involves as many as three events.

5. See students' work.

6. $\frac{1}{7776}$ or 0.0001286

7a. outcomes from tree diagram: burger, soup, lemonade; burger, soup, soft drink; burger, salad, lemonade; burger, salad, soft drink; burger, French fries, lemonade; burger, French fries, soft drink; sandwich, soup, lemonade; sandwich, soup, soft drink; sandwich, salad, lemonade; sandwich, salad, soft drink; sandwich, French fries, lemonade; sandwich, French fries, soft drink; taco, soup, lemonade; taco, soup, soft drink; taco, salad, lemonade; taco, salad, soft drink; taco, French fries, lemonade; taco, French fries, soft drink; pizza, soup, lemonade; pizza, soup, soft drink; pizza, salad, lemonade; pizza, salad, soft drink; pizza, French fries, lemonade; pizza, French fries, soft drink

7b. $\frac{1}{3}$ or $0.\overline{3}$

7c. $\frac{1}{12}$ or $0.08\overline{3}$

7d. $\frac{1}{24}$ or $0.041\overline{6}$

9a. 15

9b. $\frac{1}{5}$ or 0.2

8a. Let 1-5 represent the roads, and let A and B represent the doors.

1 — A ———	1A
1 — B ———	1B
2 — A ———	2A
2 — B ———	2B
3 — A ———	3A
3 — B ———	3B
4 — A ———	4A
4 — B ———	4B
5 — A ———	5A
5 — B ———	5B

8b. $\frac{1}{10}$ or 0.1

10. $\frac{1}{6}$ or $0.1\overline{6}$

11. $\frac{1}{3}$ or $0.\overline{3}$

12a. outcomes from tree diagram: blue, right, hand; blue, right, foot; blue, left, hand; blue, left, foot; red, right, hand; red, right, foot; red, left, hand; red, left, foot; green, right, hand; green, right, foot; green, left, hand; green, left, foot; yellow, right, hand; yellow, right, foot; yellow, left, hand; yellow, left, foot

12b. $\frac{1}{16}$ or 0.0625

13a. R3-G5, R3-R10, R3-B10, R3-G1, R3-Y14, B3-G5, B3-R10, B3-B10, B3-G1, B3-Y14, R5-G5, R5-R10, R5-B10, R5-G1, R5-Y14, R14-G5, R14-R10, R14-B10, R14-G1, R14-Y14, Y10-G5, Y10-R10, Y10-B10, Y10-G1, Y10-Y14

14a. outcomes from tree diagram: TTTTT, TTTTF, TTTFT, TTTFF, TTFTT, TTFTF, TTFFT, TTFFF, TFTTT, TFTTF, TFTFT, TFTFF, TFFTT, TFFTF, TFFFT, TFFFF, FTTTT, FTTTF, FTTFT, FTTFF, FTFTT, FTFTF, FTFFT, FTFFF, FFTTT, FFTTF, FFTFT, FFTFF, FFFTT, FFFTF, FFFFT, and FFFFF.

13b. $\frac{3}{25}$ or 0.12

13c. $\frac{2}{25}$ or 0.08

13d. 0

13e. $\frac{14}{25}$ or 0.56

14b. $\frac{13}{16}$ or 0.8125

14c. Answers will vary. See students' work.

15a. about 5.6%

15b. about 26.3%

15c. See student's work.

16. 14%

17. 32%

18a. See students' work; 30 outcomes.

18b. $\frac{1}{5}$

19. between 83 and 99, inclusive

20. $\frac{2}{3}n > 99$, $\{n \mid n > 148.5\}$

21. 3; −9

22. $r = \frac{17t - 11}{3}$

23a. 50°

23b. 130°

23c. yes

7–6 Solving Open Sentences Involving Absolute Value
Pages 423–426

1. You can graph the meaning of the absolute value inequality on a number line, or you can solve the compound inequality it represents algebraically.

2. $|x + 7| > 4$ is solved as $x + 7 > 4$ or $x + 7 > -4$; $|x + 7| < 4$ is solved as $x + 7 < 4$ and $x + 7 > -4$

3. $n = -x$

4. Yes, it will always be $\varnothing$.

5. c

6. d

7. c

8. a

9. d

10. b

11. $\{m \mid m \leq -5 \text{ or } m \geq 5\}$

$-8\ -6\ -4\ -2\ \ 0\ \ 2\ \ 4\ \ 6\ \ 8$

12. $\{n \mid -6 < n < 6\}$

$-10\ -8\ -6\ -4\ -2\ \ 0\ \ 2\ \ 4\ \ 6\ \ 8\ \ 10$

13. $\{r \mid -9 < r < 3\}$

$-12\ -10\ -8\ -6\ -4\ -2\ \ 0\ \ 2\ \ 4\ \ 6$

14. $\{t \mid t \leq 5 \text{ or } t \geq 11\}$

$3\ \ 4\ \ 5\ \ 6\ \ 7\ \ 8\ \ 9\ \ 10\ 11\ 12\ 13$

15. $|x| = 2$

16. $|x - 1| \leq 3$

17. $\{-2, 6\}$

$-6\ -4\ -2\ \ 0\ \ 2\ \ 4\ \ 6\ \ 8\ \ 10$

18. $\{1\}$

$-3\ -2\ -1\ \ 0\ \ 1\ \ 2\ \ 3\ \ 4\ \ 5$

19. $\varnothing$

20. $\{w \mid w \leq -9 \text{ or } w \geq -7\}$

$-12\ -11\ -10\ -9\ -8\ -7\ -6\ -5\ -4$

21. $\{y \mid 1 \leq y \leq 3\}$

$-2\ -1\ \ 0\ \ 1\ \ 2\ \ 3\ \ 4\ \ 5\ \ 6$

22. $\{t \mid t \leq -7 \text{ or } t \geq -1\}$

$-9\ -8\ -7\ -6\ -5\ -4\ -3\ -2\ -1\ \ 0\ \ 1$

23. $\varnothing$

24. $\left\{x \mid -\dfrac{9}{2} < x < -\dfrac{1}{2}\right\}$

$-5\quad -4\quad -3\quad -2\quad -1\quad \ 0$

25. $\left\{e \mid \dfrac{5}{3} < e < 3\right\}$

$1\qquad 2\qquad 3\qquad 4$

26. $\left\{x \mid -4 < x < \dfrac{4}{3}\right\}$

$-6\ -5\ -4\ -3\ -2\ -1\ \ 0\ \ 1\ \ 2\ \ 3\ \ 4$

27. {all numbers}

28. $\{x \mid x \neq 0\}$

A number line from −4 to 4 with an open circle at 0.

29. $\{w \mid 0 \leq w \leq 18\}$

A number line from 0 to 18 (marked by 2s) with closed endpoints at 0 and 18.

30. $\varnothing$

31. $\{-2, 3\}$

A number line from −4 to 4 with closed dots at −2 and 3.

32. $\{r \mid r \leq -1.\overline{6} \text{ or } r \geq 2\}$

A number line from −4 to 4 with shading left of about −1.6 and right of 2.

33. $\left\{x \mid x \leq -\dfrac{8}{3} \text{ or } x \geq 4\right\}$

A number line from −4 to 6 with shading left of about −2.6 and right of 4.

34. $\left\{p \mid -1 < p < \dfrac{4}{3}\right\}$

A number line from −1 to 2 with open circles at −1 and about 1.3.

35. $|p - 1| \leq 0.01$

36. $|s - 55| \leq 3$

37. $|t - 50| > 50$

38. $|x - 2| = 4$

39. $|x + 1| = 3$

40. $|x| \geq 2$

41. $|x - 1| \leq 1$

42. $|x + 1| < 3$

43. $|x - 8| \geq 3$

44. $\{-3, -2, -1, 0, 1, 2, 3\}$

45. $\{-2, -1, 0, 1, 2\}$

46. $2a - 1$

47. $2a + 1$

48. $\left\{\dfrac{1}{2}\right\}$

49. $a \neq 0$; never

50. $|x - 10| \leq 2$

51. $\dfrac{8}{13}$ or 0.61

52. $-259°\text{C} < t < 255°\text{C}$

53. no; $52 \leq s \leq 66$

54. $297.5 \leq t \leq 302.5$ minutes

A number line from 52 to 66 with closed dots at 52 and 66.

55. $\$16,500 \leq p \leq \$18,000$

56a. $2.40 \leq s \leq 43.00$; $|s - 22.70| \leq 20.30$

56b. $22 \leq s \leq 43$; $|s - 32.50| \leq 10.50$

56c. See students' work.

57a. outcomes from tree diagram: BBBB, BBBG, BBGB, BBGG, BGBB, BGBG, BGGB, BGGG, GBBB, GBBG, GBGB, GBGG, GGBB, GGBG, GGGB, GGGG

58. $\$1932 < p < \$2500$

57b. $\frac{1}{16}$ or 0.0625, regardless of gender

57c. $\frac{3}{8}$ or 0.375

59. $\{x \mid x \geq -1\}$

61. $\{k \mid k \geq -15\}$

63.

60. $\{t \mid t > -36\}$

62. $(3, 2)$

64. 1.2 in.; 1.6 in.

65. $m = -6 - \frac{n}{2}$

66. $-14r + 6$

7–7 Integration: Statistics   Box-and-Whisker Plots
Pages 429–432

1. Scale must be large enough to include the least and greatest values.

3. the median

5. Sample answer: quartiles, interquartile range, outliers, whether the data are clustered or diverse; individual point of data, number of data

7a. A: 25, 65, 30, 60, 40; B: 20, 70, 40, 60, 45

7b. B

7c. A

7d. B

2. LV and Q1; Q3 and GV

4a. 25%

4b. 90 − 120

4c. none

6a. 1985: 14.0, 18.0, 11.9, 6.1; 1992: 13.1, 15.7, 11.9, 3.8

6b. 21.5, 23.3

6c.

6d. 1992; because the plot is not as wide.

8a. A

8b. yes; A

8c. about the same

8d. B; The lives of the bulbs were more consistent.

9a. Q2 = 6.5, Q3 = 16, Q1 = 5, IQR = 11

9b. no

9c.

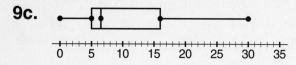

11a.

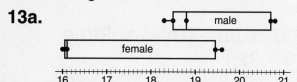

11b. clustered with lots of outliers

11c. There are four western states that have more American Indian people than other states.

11d. It is greater than the median.

13a.

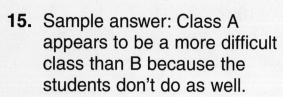

Male data are more condensed and generally higher than female data.

13b. 1990; see students' work.

15. Sample answer: Class A appears to be a more difficult class than B because the students don't do as well.

17. $\{m \mid m > 1\}$

19.

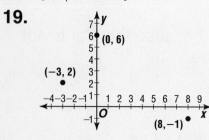

10.

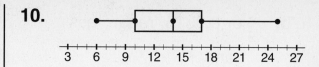

12a.

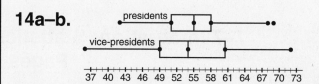

12b. 22

12c. PA

12d. the upper half

14a–b.

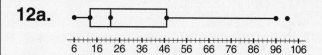

14c. The presidents seem more clustered because the box portion, representing 50% of the data, is narrower.

14d. age 66-72, assuming no vice-president age 66 or 67 succeeded a president during the president's term

16. 270 to 315 miles

18. $3x - y = 5$

20. 11

1a.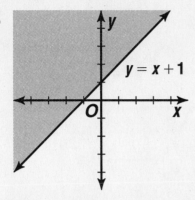

$y = x + 1$

1b. The boundary is the graph of $y = x + 1$ and it is included.

1c. The half-plane above the line is shaded.

1d. Sample answer: $(-3, 3)$

3. See students' work.

5. a

7. b

9. a, c; no

2. Replace the x and y in the inequality with the values of the ordered pair. If the inequality holds true, then the ordered pair is part of the solution set.

4. c

6. d

8. b, c; yes

10. $\{(-2, 2)\}$

11.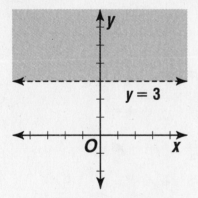

$y = 3$

12.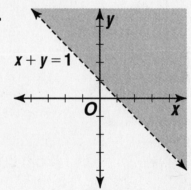

$x + y = 1$

13.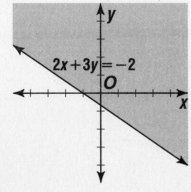

$2x + 3y = -2$

14.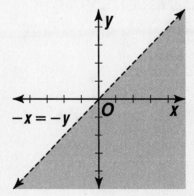

$-x = -y$

Algebra 1

15.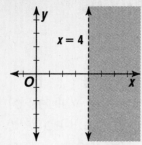

16.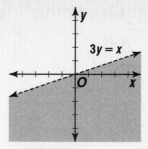

17.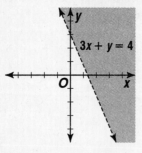

18.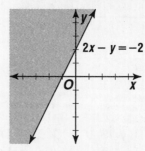

19. {(1, 1), (1, 2)}

20. {(1, 2)}

21. ∅

22.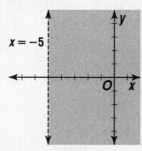

23.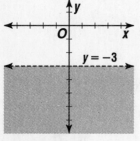

24.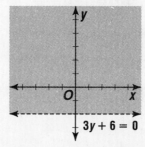

25.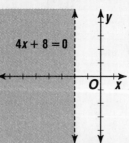

26.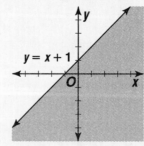

27.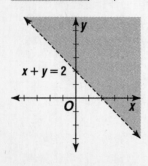

28.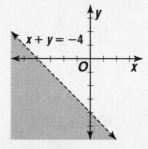

Algebra 1

29.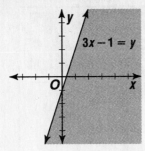

$3x - 1 = y$

30.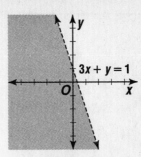

$3x + y = 1$

31.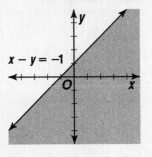

$x - y = -1$

32.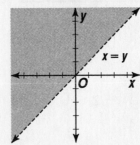

$x = y$

33.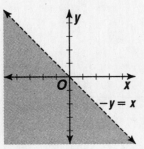

$-y = x$

34.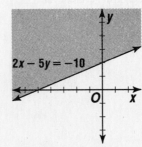

$2x - 5y = -10$

35.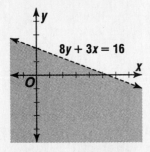

$8y + 3x = 16$

36.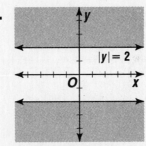

$|y| = 2$

37.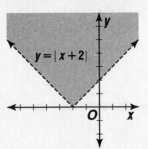

$y = |x + 2|$

38.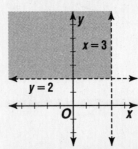

$x = 3$

$y = 2$

39.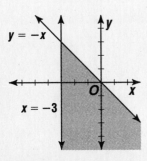

$y = -x$

$x = -3$

40.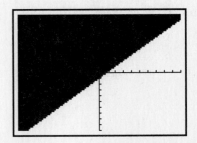

41.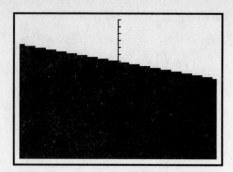

42.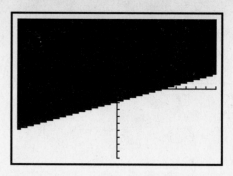

43. c

44. a, c, d

45. a, b, d

46. $\{x \geq 0 \text{ and } y \geq 0\}$ or $\{x \leq 0$ and $y \leq 0\}$; $xy \geq 0$

47a. $0.7(220 - a) \leq z \leq 0.8(220 - a)$

47b. $32 \leq z \leq 37$

47c. improve cardiovascular conditioning

48a. 1987–88, 1988–89, 1989–90

48b.

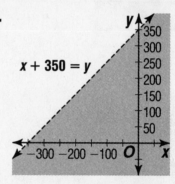

48c. See students' work.

49.

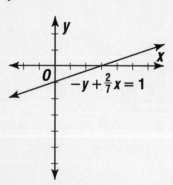

50. $\{x \mid 2 < x < 5\}$

51. $y = 4x - 2$

52. $-\dfrac{12}{5}$

53.

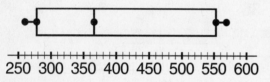

54. $\{(-1, 4), (2, 3), (0, -4), (9, 17)\}$

55. $138.22

56. 28, 29, 30

Algebra 1

Chapter 8
Solving Systems of Linear Equations and Inequalities
8–1 Graphing Systems of Equations
Pages 458–461

1. (2, 4); The graphs intersect at the point (2, 4) and (2, 4) is a solution of both equations.

2. Find an ordered pair that satisfies both equations.

3. The graphs are the same line.

4. Sample answer: (3, 0), (4, 1)

5. Sample answer:
$$x + y = 2$$
$$x - y = -8$$

6. Graphs will vary, but lines must be parallel.

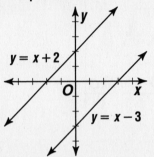

7. See students' work.

8. one; (4, 1)

9. no solution

10. one; (−3, 8)

11. one; (−6, 2)

12. no

13. yes

14. one; (0, −4)

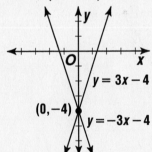

15. one; (3, 5)

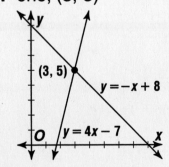

16. no solution

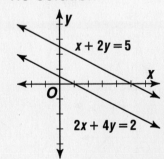

17. one; $(2, -6)$

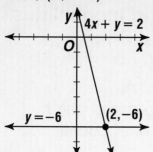

18. infinitely many

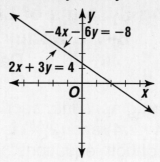

19. one; $(-6, 8)$

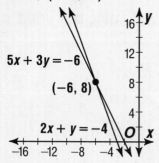

20a–b.

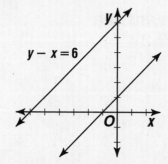

20c. The graphs of the system are parallel lines. The system has no solution and is inconsistent.

21. one; $(3, -1)$

22. one; $(6, 2)$

23. no solution

24. one; $(9, 5)$

25. one; $(3, 3)$

26. one; $(9, 1)$

27. one; $(2, -2)$

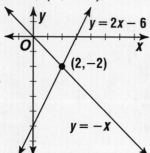

28. one; $(-3, 0)$

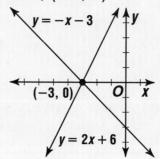

29. one; $(-1, 3)$

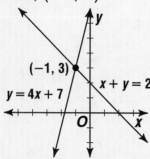

30. one; $(4, 2)$

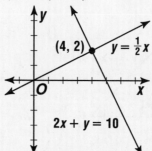

Algebra 1

31. one; $(-2, 4)$

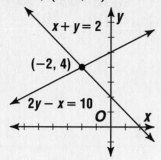

32. no solution

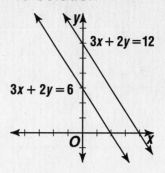

33. one; $(2, 0)$

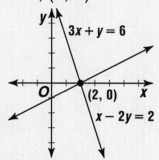

34. one; $(3, 1)$

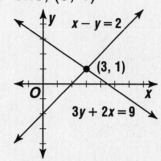

35. infinitely many

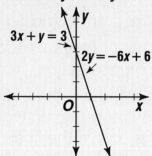

36. one; $(-1, -5)$

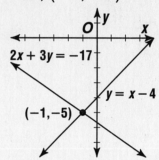

37. no solution

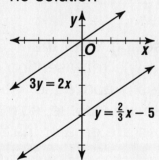

38. one; $(3, 4)$

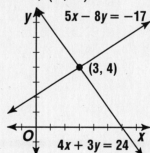

39. one; $(8, 6)$

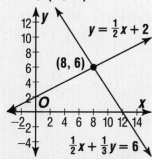

40. infinitely many

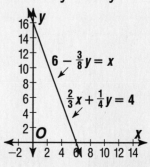

Algebra 1

41. infinitely many

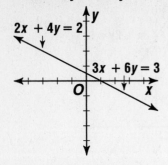

42. (2, 4), (0, 3), (−1, 10)

43. 15 square units

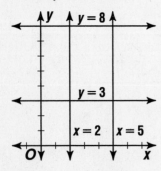

44. (−1.50, 0.50)

45. (1.71, −2.57)

46. (−0.44, 7.67)

47. (−0.25, −3.25)

48. Yes, the lines are coincident.

49. $A = -3$, $B = 2$

50a. The number of toys sold for which expenses equal income.

50b. After selling more than 1000 toys; the line representing income is above the line representing expenses, so income is greater than expenses.

50c. When selling fewer than 1000 toys; the line representing expenses is above the line representing income, so expenses are greater than income.

51.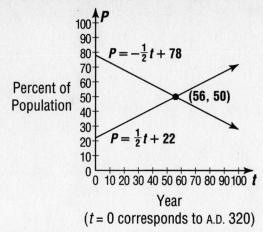

$P = -\frac{1}{2}t + 78$

Percent of Population

(56, 50)

$P = \frac{1}{2}t + 22$

Year
($t = 0$ corresponds to A.D. 320)

A.D. 376

53. $\{-1.5, -13.5\}$

55. $y = -2x + 2$

57. $7\frac{1}{2}\%$

59a. how many three- and four-bedroom homes will be built

59b. $100 - h$ or $4h$

59c. 80 homes

52.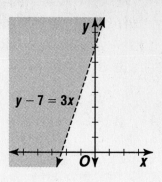

$y - 7 = 3x$

54. $\left\{p \mid p < -\frac{3}{2}\right\}$

56. 34; 466.5; 457; 439; 18

58. $-\frac{6}{b} + a$

60. 45

8–2 Substitution
Pages 466–468

1. From the first equation, y is equal to $2x - 4$, and y must have the same value in both equations.

2. There is no solution.

3. The graphs of both equations have the same slope, 9, but different y-intercepts, so the lines are parallel and the system has no solution.

4. Answers will vary.

5a. Yolanda is walking faster than Adele and catches up after about 5 seconds; 1 solution.

6. (3, 0)

5b. Yolanda never catches up with Adele because they both are walking at the same rate, and Adele has a 30-ft headstart; no solution.

5c. Yolanda never catches up with Adele because Adele is walking at a faster rate and has a 30-ft headstart.

7. $x = 8 - 4y$; $y = 2 - \frac{1}{4}x$

8. $x = 4 + \frac{5}{3}y$; $y = -\frac{12}{5} + \frac{3}{5}x$

9. $x = -\frac{0.75}{0.8} - 7.5$; $y = -\frac{0.8}{0.75}x - 8$

10. $(-3, -9)$

11. $\left(3, \frac{3}{2}\right)$

12. $(2, -1)$

13. no solution

14. $(13, 30)$

15. infinitely many

16a. $x + y = 500$, $12x + 10y = 5750$

16b. $12: 375; $10: 125

17. $(3, 1)$

18. $(5, -1)$

19. $(-4, 4)$

20. $(6, 7)$

21. $(4, -1)$

22. $(7, 2)$

23. $(2, 0)$

24. $\left(\frac{9}{2}, \frac{3}{4}\right)$

25. $(9, 1)$

26. $\left(\frac{21}{10}, \frac{7}{10}\right)$

27. $(2, 5)$

28. $(-4, 3)$

29. $(4, 2)$

30. $(50, 4)$

31. $(5, 2)$

32. infinitely many

33. $\left(\frac{8}{3}, \frac{13}{3}\right)$

34. no solution

35. $(36, -6, -84)$

36. $(-1, 5, -4)$

37. $(14, 27, -6)$

38. 40, 51, 62, 73, 84, 95

39a. $y = 1000 + 5x$, $y = 13x$

40. 20.93 gal of cream, 29.07 gal of milk

39b. 125 tickets

41a. 26.5 years

42. $750

41b. 33.8 seconds

41c. See students' work.

43a.

	75% Gold (18-carat)	50% Gold (12-carat)	58% Gold (14-carat)
Total Grams	x	y	300
Grams of Pure Gold	$0.75x$	$0.50y$	$0.58(300)$

43b. $x + y = 300$
$0.75x + 0.50y = 0.58(300)$

43c. 96 grams of 18-carat gold, 204 grams of 12-carat gold

45. 37 shares

47. {$(-1, -7)$, $(4, 8)$, $(7, 17)$, $(13, 35)$}

49. -3

51. $m - 12$

44. infinitely many

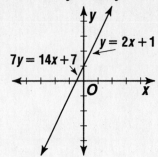

46.

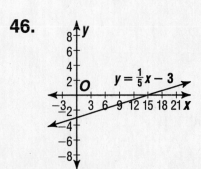

48. 70.5

50.

$$-5\ -4\ -3\ -2\ -1\ \ 0\ \ 1$$

8–3 Elimination Using Addition and Subtraction
Pages 472–474

1a. When the coefficients of one of the variables are the same.

1b. When the coefficients of one of the variables are additive inverses of each other.

3. Both are correct. If the resulting statement is false, there is no solution. If the resulting statement is true, there is an infinite number of solutions

5. addition, $(1, 0)$

7. subtraction, $\left(-\frac{5}{2}, -2\right)$

9. substitution, $(1, 4)$

2a. The result is $0 = 45$, which is false. Thus, the system has no solution.

2b. The graph is two parallel lines.

4a. Sample answer: $(-3, 4)$

4b. $(-3.4, 4.2)$

6. substitution, $(1, 2)$

8. subtraction, $\left(\frac{3}{16}, -\frac{1}{2}\right)$

10. substitution, $(0, 2)$

11. 8, 48

12a. $(-2, 1)$

12b. $\left(-\dfrac{19}{9}, \dfrac{4}{3}\right)$

13a. $(1, -4)$

13b. $(1.29, -4.05)$

14a. $(-2, 3)$

14b. $\left(-\dfrac{17}{9}, \dfrac{19}{6}\right)$

15. addition; $(6, 2)$

16. addition; $(2, 1)$

17. subtraction; $(4, -1)$

18. subtraction; $(-5, 20)$

19. subtraction; $(4, -7)$

20. addition or subtraction; $\left(\dfrac{9}{2}, 2\right)$

21. addition; $(5, 1)$

22. subtraction; $(7, 4)$

23. substitution; infinitely many

24. subtraction; $(-5, 4)$

25. subtraction; $(-2, 3)$

26. subtraction; $\left(2, -\dfrac{3}{2}\right)$

27. subtraction; $\left(\dfrac{1}{2}, 1\right)$

28. substitution; $\varnothing$

29. addition; $(10, -15)$

30. substitution; $(1.5, 0)$

31. addition; $(1.75, 2.5)$

32. subtraction; $(15.8, 3.4)$

33. 11, 53

34. 20, -2

35. 5, 8

36. 24

37. $(2, 3, 7)$

38. $(4, 2, 3)$

39. $(14, 27, -6)$

40 $(2, 1)$

41. Ling, 1.45 hours or 1 hour, 27 minutes; José, 1.15 hours, or 1 hour, 9 minutes

42a. $(693.75, 58.125)$

42b. 480 ft

43. 320 gal of 25% and 180 gal of 50%

44. $\left\{h \mid h \geq -\dfrac{1}{2}\right\}$

45. -3

46.

47. $-\dfrac{7}{6}$

48. 3.87

49. substitution $(=)$

1. one; (1, −2)

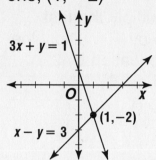

2. no solution

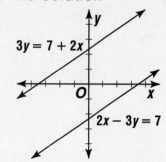

3. infinitely many

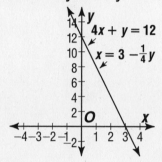

4. (2, 10)

5. (−9, −7)
7. (10, 15)
9. (4, −2)

6. (4, 3)
8. (3, 1)
10. $15 for members, $45 for nonmembers

8–4 Elimination Using Multiplication
Pages 478–481

1. See students' work.

2. To make either the *x*-term or *y*-term coefficients additive inverses.

3. Sample answer: $3x + 5y = 7$, $4x - 10y = 1$

4. See students' work.

5. (−1, 1); Multiply the first equation by −3, then add.

6. (2, −2); Multiply the first equation by 3, multiply the second equation by −2, then add.

Algebra 1

7. $(-9, -13)$; Multiply the second equation by 5, then add.

8. $(5, -2)$; Multiply the first equation by 5, multiply the second equation by -7, then add.

9. $(-1, -2)$; Multiply the first equation by 5, multiply the second equation by -8, then add.

10. $(4, 2)$; Multiply the first equation by 4, multiply the second equation by 3, then add.

11. b; $(2, 0)$

12. a; $(-3, -1)$

13. c; $(4, 1)$

14a. 15 mph

14b. 3 mph

15. $(2, 1)$

16. $(6, 4)$

17. $(5, -2)$

18. $(2, 4)$

19. $(2, -5)$

20. $(2, -3)$

21. $(-4, -7)$

22. $(5, -5)$

23. $(-1, -2)$

24. $(2, -8)$

25. $(4, -6)$

26. $(10, 25)$

27. $(13, -2)$

28. $(5, 1)$

29. $(10, 12)$

30. 86

31. 6, 9

32. 28

33. elimination, addition; $\left(2, \frac{1}{8}\right)$

34. elimination, multiplication; $(-2, 1)$

35. substitution or elimination, multiplication; infinitely many

36. elimination, multiplication; $(3, -1)$

37. elimination, subtraction; $(24, 4)$

38. elimination, multiplication; $(-6, -8)$

39. $(11, 12)$

40. $\left(\frac{1}{5}, \frac{1}{2}\right)$

41. $\left(\frac{1}{3}, \frac{1}{6}\right)$

42a. infinitely many

42b. $(-9, -7)$

42c. no solution

42d. infinitely many

43. $(-2, 7), (2, 2), (7, 5)$

44. $(35, 25)$

45. 6 2-seat tables, 11 4-seat tables

46. $0.45 and $0.15

47. $(3, -4)$

48. 35

49. $\frac{1}{3}$

50. $(-1, 5)$

51. 165 yd

52. 1

53. 2 cups

54. 8

8–5 Graphing Systems of Inequalities
Pages 484–486

1. A boundary line is included in the graph if the inequality is $\leq$ or $\geq$ and not included if the inequality is $<$ or $>$.

2. Rolanda is correct; Sample answer: $y < 2x + 4$ and $y > x - 1$; the solution of $y = 2x + 4$ and $y = x - 1$, $(-5, -6)$, is not a solution to the system of inequalities.

3. Sample answer: $y < x + 1$ and $y > x + 3$. There is no intersection.

4a. yes

4b. yes

4c. no

4d. no

5. Answers will vary.

6.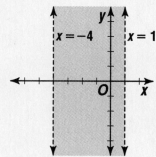

7.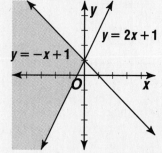

8.

9.

10.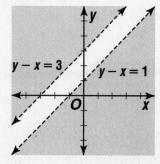

11.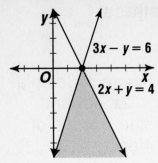

$3x - y = 6$

$2x + y = 4$

12. $y \leq -x + 3; y \leq x + 3$

13. $y > x, y \leq x + 4$

14. Sample answer:
7 pepperoni, 1 supreme;
5 pepperoni, 3 supreme;
2 pepperoni, 5 supreme

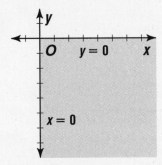

$9.95x + 12.95y = 90$

$x + y = 6$

15.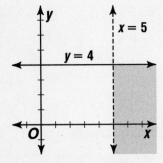

$x = 5$

$y = 4$

16.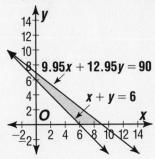

$y = 0$

$x = 0$

17.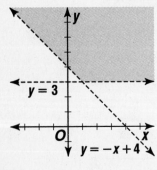

$y = 3$

$y = -x + 4$

18.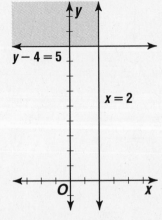

$y - 4 = 5$

$x = 2$

19.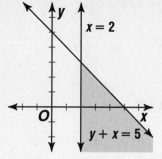

$x = 2$

$y + x = 5$

20.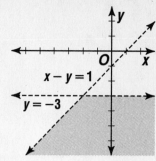

$x - y = 1$

$y = -3$

21.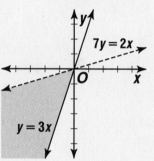

$y = 2x + 3$

$y = -x + 1$

22.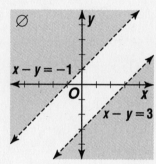

$y - x = 3$

$y - x = 2$

23.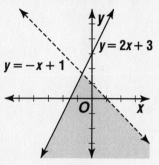

$7y = 2x$

$y = 3x$

24.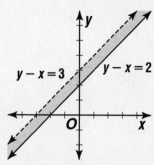

$\varnothing$

$x - y = -1$

$x - y = 3$

25.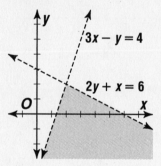

$3x - y = 4$

$2y + x = 6$

26.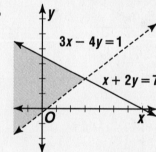

$3x - 4y = 1$

$x + 2y = 7$

27.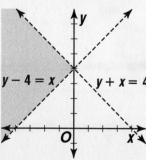

$y - 4 = x$

$y + x = 4$

28.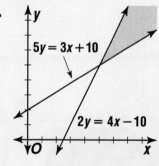

$5y = 3x + 10$

$2y = 4x - 10$

29.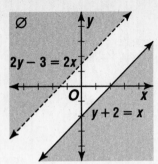

$\varnothing$

$2y - 3 = 2x$

$y + 2 = x$

30.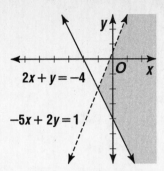

$2x + y = -4$

$-5x + 2y = 1$

31.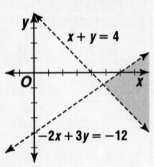

$x + y = 4$

$-2x + 3y = -12$

32.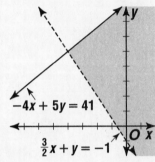

$-4x + 5y = 41$

$\frac{3}{2}x + y = -1$

33. $y > -1, x \geq -2$

35. $y \leq x, y > x - 3$

37. $x \geq 0, y \geq 0, x + 2y \leq 6$

34. $3x - 5y \geq -25, y \geq 0, x \leq 0$

36. $2x - 3y \geq -6, x + y > -3$

38. $4x - 3y \geq -12, 2x + y \leq 4, x + 2y \geq 2$

39.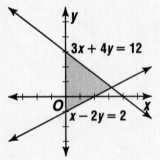

$3x + 4y = 12$

$x - 2y = 2$

40.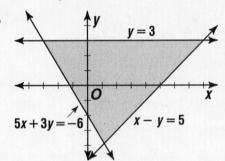

$y = 3$

$5x + 3y = -6$

$x - y = 5$

41.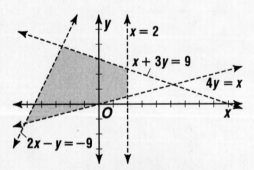

$x = 2$

$x + 3y = 9$

$4y = x$

$2x - y = -9$

42.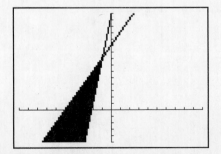

43.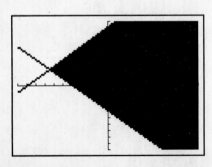

44.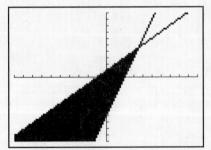

Algebra 1

45.

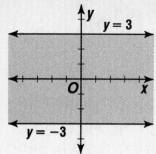

46. Sample answers: 3 ounces of mozzarella, 4 ounces of Swiss; 4 ounces of mozzarella, 3 ounces of Swiss; 5 ounces of mozzarella, 3 ounces of Swiss

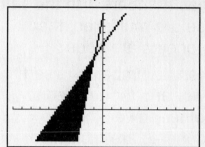

47. Sample answer: walk 15 min, jog 15 min; walk 10 min, jog 20 min; walk 5 min, jog 25 min

48. 24

49. 4 $5 bills, 8 $20 bills

50. $\{a \mid -2 > a > 31\}$

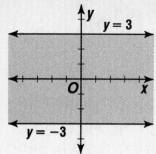

51. $y = -\dfrac{1}{2}x + \dfrac{9}{2}$

52. $\{2, 1, 0\}$

53. 10

54. 12 miles

55. Let y = the number of yards gained in both games; $y = 134 + (134 - 17)$

56. associative $(\times)$

Chapter 9 Exploring Polynomials
9–1 Multiplying Monomials
Pages 499–500

1a. When numbers with the same base are multiplied, the exponents are added.

1b. When a number is raised to a power and then raised to another power, the two exponents are multiplied.

1c. When two numbers are multiplied and the product is raised to a power, each number can be raised to the power before multiplying.

3. Taryn is correct. When numbers with the same base are multiplied, the exponents are added, the bases aren't multiplied.

2. If the bases are different you cannot add the exponents. $2^3 \cdot 3^2 = 8 \cdot 9 = 72$ is not the same as $(2 \cdot 3)^{3+2}$ or 6^5.

4. Answers will vary. Sample answers: 2^6, $(2^3)^2$, $2^2 \times 2^4$, 2×2^5, $2^3 \times 2^3$, $(2^2)^2 \times 2^2$

5. no

6. yes

7. no

8. no

9. a^{12}

10. $x^3 y^7$

11. 3^{16} or 43,046,721

12. $4a^4 b^2$

13. $9a^2 y^6$

14. $x^4 y^4$

15. $15a^4 b^3$

16. b^9

17. $m^4 n^3$

18. $a^7 b^5$

19. 2^{12} or 4096

20. $12x^8 y^4$

21. $a^{12} x^8$

22. $m^{10} b^2$

23. $6x^4 y^4 z^4$

24. $0.216d^3$

25. $a^2 b^2 c^2$

26. $-10a^3 c$

27. $\frac{4}{25} d^2$

28. $-3a^2 x^6 y^2$

29. $0.09x^6 y^4$

30. $-54a^3 b^6$

31. $90y^{10}$

32. $x^4 y^4$

33. $4a^3 b^5$

34. $29a^6$

35. $-520x^9$

36. For example, $(x + y)^2 = (x + y)(x + y)$ and not $x^2 + y^2$.

37. -2^4 equals $-(2)(2)(2)(2)$ or -16 and $(-2)^4$ equals $(-2)(-2)(-2)(-2)$ or 16.

38a. $14,336.30
38b. $15,811.21

39. 301 parts

40. $x \le 2, y \ge 2$

41. one; $(-6, 3)$

42. 2300 cards

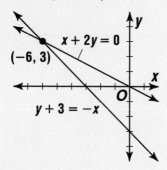

43. $n = 2m + 1$

m	-3	-2	-1	0	1
n	-5	-3	-1	**1**	**3**

44. 43.2 mph

45. $136°$

46. -2

47. $1.11y + 0.06$

9–2 Dividing by Monomials
Pages 503–505

1. $\dfrac{0^m}{0^m} \ne 0^{m-m}$, because $0^m = 0$ and division by 0 is not defined.

2. Division by 0 is not defined.

3. Since each number is obtained by dividing the previous number by 3, $3^1 = 3$ and $3^0 = 1$.

4. Divide the previous number by 5.

5^5	5^4	5^3	5^2	5^1	5^0	5^{-1}	5^{-2}	5^{-3}	5^{-4}
3125	625	125	25	5	1	$\dfrac{1}{5}$	$\dfrac{1}{25}$	$\dfrac{1}{125}$	$\dfrac{1}{625}$

5. See students' work.

6. See students' work.

7. $\dfrac{1}{121}$

8. $\dfrac{1}{1296}$

9. 36

10. $\dfrac{1}{a^3}$

11. $\dfrac{6}{r^4}$

12. $a^{10}b^6$

13. $\dfrac{\pi}{4}$

14. $\dfrac{1}{b^2c}$

15. a^2

16. $\dfrac{5}{n^3}$

17. m^6

18. $\dfrac{b^2}{d^6}$

19. $\dfrac{m^3}{3}$

20. $-y^2 m^{15}$

21. $\dfrac{c^3}{b^8}$

22. $-2ab^4 c^5$

23. b^8

24. $\dfrac{7x^3}{4z^{10}}$

25. $-s^6$

26. $\dfrac{1}{25r^8}$

27. $-\dfrac{4b^3}{c^3}$

28. $\dfrac{9ab^6}{5c^6}$

29. $\dfrac{1}{64a^6}$

30. 1

31. $\dfrac{s^3}{r^3}$

32. $\dfrac{m}{7rn}$

33. $\dfrac{a}{4c^2}$

34. $\dfrac{16y^6}{9x^6 z^2}$

35. m^{3+n}

36. y^{2c+5c}

37. 3^{4x-6}

38. $\dfrac{1}{r^5}$

39. $\dfrac{1}{q^{18}}$

40. y^{2x-a}

41. $1257.14

42. $6645.57

43. $98a^5 b^4$

44. 425 mph

45. $|x+1| + < 3$

46. $-\dfrac{7}{10} > z$

47. $(3, -5)$

48. $31.00

49. $\dfrac{52}{41}$

50. $82y$

9–3 Scientific Notation
Pages 509–512

1. when the number is greater than or equal to 10

2. when the number is less than 1

3. In your head, first multiply 1.2 and 4 and then multiply 10^5 and 10^8. The answer is 4.8×10^{13}.

4. In your head, first divide 4.4 by 4 and then divide 10^4 by 10^7. The answer is 1.1×10^{-3}.

5. 43,400,000; 1.515×10^3

6. 94,600,000; 3.963×10^3

7. 507,000,000; 4.4419×10^4

8. 1,859,700,000; 1.5881×10^4

9. 4,551,400,000; 7.14×10^2

10. 5.09×10^{-5} cm

11. 1.672×10^{-21} mg

12. 1.1×10^{-4} mm

13. 4×10^{-6} in

14. 2.1708×10^8; 217,080,000

15. 6.2×10^{-7}; 0.00000062

16. 3×10^5; 300,000

17. 6×10^7; 60,000,000

18. 9.5×10^3

19. 9.5×10^{-3}

20. 5.69×10

21. 8.76×10^{10}

22. 7.61×10^{-10}

23. 3.1272×10^8

24. 8×10^{-8}

25. 9.0909×10^{-2}

26. 3.55×10^9

27. 7.86×10^4

28. 1.12×10^{-6}

29. 7×10^{-10}

30. 7.83×10

31. 9.9×10^{-6}

32. 4.48×10^6; 4,480,000

33. 6×10^{-3}; 0.006

34. 2.088×10^{10}; 20,880,000,000

35. 8.992×10^{-7}; 0.0000008992

36. 4×10^7; 40,000,000

37. 4×10^{-2}; 0.04

38. 2.3×10^{-6}; 0.0000023

39. 6.5×10^{-6}; 0.0000065

40. 3×10^{-5}; 0.00003

41. 6.6×10^{-6}; 0.0000066

42. 7.1842×10^6; 7,184,200

43. 1.2×10^{-4}; 0.00012

44. 2.7504×10^9

45. 2.4336×10^{-1}

46. 3.5×10^{-4}

47. 2.8×10^5

48a. 1.416E7

48b. 8.84736E5

48c. 5.706E14

48d. 3.3092E4

49a. Sample answer: overflow

50. about 6.57×10^6 times greater

49b. Multiply 3.7 and 5.6 and multiply 10^{112} and 10^{10}. Then write the product in scientific notation.

49c. 2.072×10^{123}

51. 1,000,000,000,001

52. 1.5309×10^7;
9.227×10^6;
9.022×10^6;
5.460×10^6;
5.153×10^6

53. 6.75×10^{18} molecules

54a. 0.3 mm to 2 mm

54b. The smallest bacteria would probably not be seen with such a microscope.

55a. about 0.25 kg

55b. Answers may vary.

57.

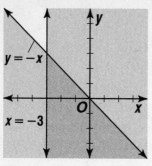

59. 25%

61. $y = x + 5$

63. yes

65. $27°$

67. -163

56. $-4y^4z^2$

58. $(-52, -20)$

60.

$$\xleftarrow{\quad}\overset{\overset{\displaystyle -4\ -3\ -2\ -1\ \ 0\ \ 1\ \ 2\ \ 3\ \ 4}{}}{\rule{0pt}{0pt}}\xrightarrow{\quad}$$

62. -232 ft/mi or about -0.044

64. {4, 0, 21, 13, 3}

66. 26.385, 26.58

9–4 Polynomials
Pages 516–519

1. $-27 = -27x^0$

3. Sample answers:
poly- more than one
polygon, a plane closed figure formed by several line segments; *polygraph*, an instrument used to measure several different pulsations at one time.
mono- one
monologue, a conversation by one person; *monotone*, a series of sounds in the same key or pitch

5. yes; trinomial

7. yes; binomial

9. 0

11. $x^8 - 12x^6 + 5x^3 - 11x$

13a. $\ell\, w - \pi r^2 - s^2$

2. $\dfrac{34}{n}$ is not a monomial.

bi- two
bicycle, a vehicle with two wheels; *bifocal*, eyeglasses with two focal lengths
tri- three
triangle, a polygon with three sides; *tricycle*, vehicle with three wheels

4. $2x^2 - 2x - 3$

6. no

8. 1

10. 15

12. $y^4x - x^2 + y^5x^3 + yx^5$

14. yes; monomial

13b. about 91.43 square units

15. yes; trinomial

16. no

17. yes; binomial

18. no

19. yes; trinomial

20. 2

21. 5

22. 0

23. 3

24. 6

25. 9

26. 1

27. 4

28. 7

29. $x^5 + 3x^3 + 5$

30. $-2x^5 - 9x^2y + 8x + 5$

31. $-x^7 + abx^2 - bcx + 34$

32. $\frac{12}{19}x^{12} - 14x^7 + 9ax^2 + 7a^3x$

33. $1 + x^2 + x^3 + x^5$

34. $y^4 + 3xy^4 - x^2y^3 + 4x^3y$

35. $7a^3x + \frac{2}{3}x^2 - 8a^3x^3 + \frac{1}{5}x^5$

36. $4 + \frac{2}{3}x - x^2 + \frac{3}{4}x^3y$

37. $2ab + \pi b^2$; about 353.10 square units

38. $2ar - \pi r^2$; about 121.46 square miles

39. $ab - 4x^2$; 116 square units

40. $2bc - \frac{1}{2}\pi c^2$; about 17.72 square units

41a. See students' work.

41b. $8a^4 + 9a^3 + 4a^2 + 3a^1 + 5a^0$

42. Yes; after 6 years she has $53,070.58.

43. about 153 eggs

44a. $\pi r^2h + \frac{2}{3}\pi r^3$

44b. about 9114.81 ft^3

45. 4.235×10^4

46. (0, 25)

47. 7, 8, 9

48. 39,000 covers

49. $\left\{(-3, 8), \left(1, \frac{8}{3}\right), (3, 0), (9, -8)\right\}$

50. $\frac{5}{31}$

51. $38.75

52. $\frac{ax - 2cz}{b}$

9–5 Adding and Subtracting Polynomials
Pages 524–527

1. Align like terms.

2. Sample answer: $2a^2b^3$, $-4a^2b^3$, a^2b^3, $-a^2b^3$

3. Add your answer to the polynomial being subtracted. The sum should equal the first polynomial.

4. Find the additive inverse of the polynomial being subtracted and then add.

5a. $x^2 + 2x + 8$

5b. $-x^2 + 6x - 2$

7. $6a^2 - 3$

9. $4x^2 + 3y^2 - 8y - 7x$

11. $-8y^2$ and $3y^2$; $2x$ and $4x$

13. $3p^3q$ and $10p^3q$; $-2p$ and $-p$

15. $6m^2n^2 + 8mn - 28$

17. $-4y^2 + 5y + 3$

19. $7p^3 - 3p^2 - 2p - 7$

21. $10x^2 + 13xy$

23. $4a^3 + 2a^2b - b^2 + b^3$

25. $-4a + 6b - 5c$

27. $3a - 11m$

29. $-2n^2 + 7n + 5$

31. $13x - 2y$

33. $-y^3 + 3y + 3$

35. $4z^3 - 2z^2 + z$

37. $2x + 3y$

39. $353 - 18x$

41. $-2n^2 - n + 4$

43. $719x^2$ cubic stories

45. $-3x - 2x^3 + 4x^5$

6. $-5y + 7z$

8. $-7y^2 + 3x^2 - 2$

10. $3m$ and $6m$; $8n$ and $5n$

12. $5xy$, $14xy$, and $12xy$

14. $7ax^2 + 3a^2x - 5ax + 2x$

16. $-3x^2 + 6x$

18. $5b - 12ab + 12a$

20a. $(181 - 7x)°$

20b. $31°$, $73°$, $76°$

22. $x^2y^2 - 5xy - 10$

24. $-2a^2 - 2a - 15$

26. $8x^2 - 6x + 15$

28. $8 - 6a + 2a^2$

30. $2x^2 - 8x - 8$

32. $3ax^2 + 11ax - 4$

34. $6p^2 - p - 18$

36. $x^3 + 2x^2 + 2x - 6$

38. $10x^2 - 31x + 14$

40. $413 - 2x^2 + 3x$

42a. $x \geq 8$

42b. 19 in.

42c. 8488 sq. in.; 836 sq. in.

42d. As height increases, volume decreases.

44a. 1, 4, 9, 16, 25

44b. square numbers

44c. 36, 49, 64

44d. square numbers less than or equal to n

46. $8405.68

47. (3, 1)

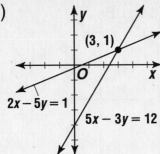

$2x - 5y = 1$

$5x - 3y = 12$

48. 135

49. Sample answer: Let $h = $ the number of hours for the repair and $c = $ the total charge; $c = 34h + 15$

50. $136,150

51. $-\dfrac{50}{3}$

52. 4 tennis balls

Self Test
Page 527

1. $-6n^5y^7$

2. $9a^4b^{10}$

3. $-12ab^4$

4. $\dfrac{125}{r^3s^3}$

5. 5.67×10^6

6. 8.6×10^{-5}

7. about 1.53×10^4 seconds or 4.25 hours

8. $4; 2a - 3x + 11x^2 + 7ax^3$

9. $5x^2 - 4x - 14$

10. $-2a^2 - 6a + 4$

9–6 Multiplying a Polynomial by a Monomial
Pages 531–533

1. distributive property

2a. Multiply 7 times $x^2 + 14x$.

2b. $7x^2 + 98x$

2c. 1232 in²

3a. Replace x with $\frac{19}{11}$ and check to see if both sides of the equation represent the same number.

3b. $x(x+3) + 7x - 5$
$= x(8+x) - 9x + 14$

$\frac{19}{11}\left(\frac{19}{11} + 3\right) + 7\left(\frac{19}{11}\right) - 5$

$= \frac{19}{11}\left(8 + \frac{19}{11}\right) - 9\left(\frac{19}{11}\right) + 14$

$\frac{19}{11}\left(\frac{52}{11}\right) + \frac{133}{11} - \frac{55}{11}$

$= \frac{19}{11}\left(\frac{107}{11}\right) - \frac{171}{11} + \frac{154}{11}$

$\frac{988}{121} + \frac{1463}{121} - \frac{605}{121}$

$= \frac{2033}{121} - \frac{1881}{121} + \frac{1694}{121}$

$\frac{1846}{121} = \frac{1846}{121}$

5. $-63b^4c - 7b$

7. $10y^2 - 26y$

9. $3w^2 - 2w$

11. $\frac{103}{19}$

13a. $a^2 + a$

13b. $a^2 + 2a$

15. $\frac{1}{3}x^2 - 9x$

17. $-20m^5 - 8m^4$

19. $30m^5 - 40m^4n + 60m^3n^3$

21. $-28d^3 + 16d^2 - 12d$

23. $-32r^2s^2 - 56r^2s + 112rs^2$

25. $\frac{36}{5}x^3y + x^3 - 24x^2y$

27. $36t^2 - 42$

29. $61y^3 - 16y^2 + 167y - 18$

31. $53a^3 - 57a^2 + 7a$

33. $-\frac{77}{8}$

4a.

4b. $6x^2 + 9x$

6. $-32a^5c + 4a^2c - 44a^2$

8. $22a^2b^2 - 55a^2b$

10. $8y^4 - 32y^3 + 5y^2 + 12y$

12. $\frac{1}{2}$

14. $-14x - 63$

16. $15s^3t + 6s^2t^2$

18. $12d^3 - 24d^2 - 45d$

20. $35x^4y - 21x^3y^2 + 7x^2y^2$

22. $10m^4 - 14m^3 + 16m^2$

24. $-\frac{1}{4}a^2b^3c - \frac{1}{3}a^2b^2 + \frac{9}{2}ab^2$

26. $4b^2 + 9b$

28. $-50m^3 + 16m^2 - 92m + 132$

30. $6t^4 + 21t^2 - \frac{33}{2}t$

32. 2

34. $\frac{1}{3}$

35. 0

36. $\frac{7}{4}$

37. $\frac{23}{24}$

38. 17

39. 2

40. $x^2 + 6x$

41. $15p^2 + 32p$

42. $12a^3 - 17a^2b + 15a^2 + 10b + 10$

43. Sample answer:
$1(8a^2b + 18ab)$; $a(8ab + 18b)$;
$b(8a^2 + 18a)$; $2(4a^2b + 9ab)$;
$(2a)(4ab + 9b)$; $(2b)(4a^2 + 9a)$;
$(ab)(8a + 18)$; $(2ab)(4a + 9)$

44a. $14y^2 + 7y$

44b. 1197 in²

45. $1.50t + 1.25mt$

46. 4.5 ft

47a.

0 diagonals
$\frac{1}{2}(3)(3 - 3) = \frac{1}{2}(3)(0)$
$\qquad\qquad\qquad = 0$

2 diagonals
$\frac{1}{2}(4)(4 - 3) = \frac{1}{2}(4)(1)$
$\qquad\qquad\qquad = 2$

5 diagonals
$\frac{1}{2}(5)(5 - 3) = \frac{1}{2}(5)(2)$
$\qquad\qquad\qquad = 5$

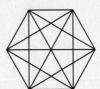

9 diagonals
$\frac{1}{2}(6)(6 - 3) = \frac{1}{2}(6)(3)$
$\qquad\qquad\qquad = 9$

47b. $\frac{1}{2}n^2 - \frac{3}{2}n$

48. $-4a - 4ab + 10b$

47c. 90 diagonals

49. 75 gal of 50%, 25 gal of 30%

50. $\frac{5}{4}$

51. $a^2 - 1$

52.

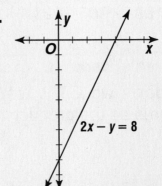

$2x - y = 8$

53. 11 days

54. 23°

55. 25.7

9–7 Multiplying Polynomials
Pages 538–541

1a. Sample answer:

$(42)(27) = (40 + 2)(20 + 7)$

      F   O   I   L

$= 40(20) + 40(7) + 2(20) + 2(7)$

$= 800 + 280 + 40 + 14$

$= 1134$

1b. Sample answer:

$$\left(4\frac{1}{2}\right)\left(6\frac{3}{4}\right) = \left(4 + \frac{1}{2}\right)\left(6 + \frac{3}{4}\right)$$

      F   O   I   L

$$= 4(6) + 4\left(\frac{3}{4}\right) + \frac{1}{2}(6) + \frac{1}{2}\left(\frac{3}{4}\right)$$

$$= 24 + 3 + 3 + \frac{3}{8}$$

$$= 30\frac{3}{8}$$

2. See students' work.

3.

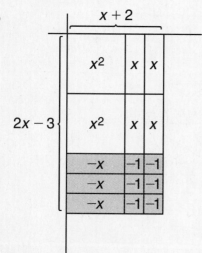

4. Sample answer: $(a + x)(2x + 3)$

5. $d^2 + 10d + 16$

6. $r^2 - 16r + 55$

7. $y^2 - 4y - 21$

8. $15p^2 - 19p - 10$

9. $2x^2 + 9x - 5$

10. $6m^2 - m - 40$

11. $10a^2 + 11ab - 6b^2$

12. $6x^3 - 25x^2 + 33x - 20$

13a. $a^3 + 3a^2 + 2a$

14. $y^2 + 12y + 35$

13b. See students' work.

13c. See students' work. The result is the same as the product in part b.

15. $c^2 - 10c + 21$

16. $x^2 - 4x - 32$

17. $w^2 - 6w - 27$

18. $2a^2 + 15a - 8$

19. $10b^2 - b - 3$

20. $132y^2 + 174 + 54$

21. $169x^2 - 9$

22. $24x^2 + 83xy + 63y^2$

23. $0.15v^2 - 2.9v - 14$

24. $6x^2 + \frac{1}{3}x - \frac{1}{27}$

25. $\frac{2}{3}a^2 + \frac{1}{18}ab - \frac{1}{3}b^2$

26. $10r^2 - 0.1r - 0.03$

27. $0.63p^2 + 3.9pq + 6q^2$

28. $x^3 + 12x^2 + 26x - 63$

29. $6x^3 + 11x^2 - 68x + 55$

30. $5a^3 - 13a^2 + 49a + 22$

31. $9x^3 - 45x^2 + 62x - 16$

32. $5x^4 - 2x^3 - 32x^2 + 14x + 11$

33. $20d^4 - 9d^3 + 73d^2 - 39d + 99$

34. $2x^4 - 20x^3 + 39x^2 - 68x - 9$

35. $10x^4 + 3x^3 + 51x^2 - 16x - 48$

36. $-35b^5 + 14b^4 - 18b^3 - 19b^2 + 14b - 12$

37. $a^4 - a^3 - 8a^2 - 29a - 35$

38. $2a^3 + 10a^2 - 2a - 10$

39. $63y^3 - 57y^2 - 36y$

40. $15x^3 + 12x^2$

41a. 28 cm, 20 cm, 16 cm

42. $3x^3 + 14x^2 + 6x - 6$

41b. 8960 cm³

41c. 8960

41d. They are the same measure.

43. $-8x^4 - 6x^3 + 24x^2 - 12x + 80$

44. $3x^5 + 13x^4 + 12x^3 + 18x^2 + 12x - 16$

45. $-3x^3 - 5x^2 - 6x + 24$

46. 20 yd by 25 yd

47a. Sample answer: $x - 2$, $x + 3$

48. $\frac{9}{2}a^2 + 9a$

47b. Sample answer: $x^2 + x - 6$

47c. bigger, 2 sq ft

49. $\{y \mid y < -6\}$

50. 2030 ft

51. $y = 2x + 1$

52. {8, 4, 6, 5}; {1, 2, −4, −3, 0}; {(1, 8), (2, 4), (−4, 6), (−3, 5), (0, 6)}

53. $a = 4$, $y = 9$

54. $363; $364

55. 15°C

56. 8

9–8 Special Products
Pages 546–547

1. The middle terms have different signs.

2. The square of a difference is $(a - b)^2$, which equals $a^2 - 2ab + b^2$. The difference of two squares is the product $(a + b)(a - b)$ or $a^2 - b^2$.

3. $(30 - 1)(30 + 1) = 900 - 1$ or 899

4a.

	x	y
x	x^2	xy
y	xy	y^2

4b.

	x	$-y$
x	x^2	$-xy$
y	$-xy$	y^2

5. $(a - b)^2 = a^2 - 2ab + b^2$

6. $4x^2 + 12xy + 9y^2$

7. $m^2 - 6mn + 9n^2$

8. $4a^2 - 9$

9. $m^4 + 8m^2n + 16n^2$

10. $16y^2 - 4z^2$

11. $25 - 10x + x^2$

12. $16x^2 + 80x + 100$ square units

13. $x^2 + 8xy + 16y^2$

14. $m^2 - 4mn + 4n^2$

15. $9b^2 - 6ab + a^2$

16. $9x^2 - 25$

17. $81p^2 - 4q^2$

18. $25s^2 + 60st + 36t^2$

19. $25b^2 - 120ab + 144a^2$

20. $4a^2 + 2ay + 0.25y^2$

21. $x^6 + 2x^3a^2 + a^4$

22. $\frac{1}{4}b^4 - a^2b^2 + a^4$

23. $64x^4 - 9y^2$

24. $49c^4 - d^6$

25. $1.21g^2 + 2.2gh^5 + h^{10}$

26. $81 - z^{18}$

27. $\frac{16}{9}x^4 - y^2$

28. $\frac{1}{9}v^4 - \frac{1}{3}v^2w^3 + \frac{1}{4}w^6$

29. $9x^3 - 45x^2 - x + 5$

30. $x^4 - 29x^2 + 100$

31. $a^3 + 9a^2b + 27ab^2 + 27b^3$

32. $16m^4 - 32m^3n + 24m^2n^2 - 8mn^3 + n^4$

33. $x^2 + y^2 + z^2 + 2xy + 2yz + 2xz$

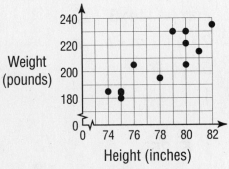

	x	y	z
x	x^2	xy	xz
y	xy	y^2	yz
z	xz	yz	z^2

35a. $2\pi s + 7\pi$ square meters

35b. about 28.27 square meters

35c. about 40.84 square meters

37. $6t^2 - 3t - 3$

39a.

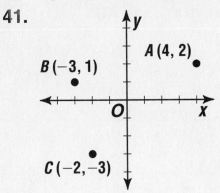

39b. the taller the player, the greater the weight

41.

A (4, 2)

B (−3, 1)

O   X

C (−2, −3)

43. 5

34a.

	t	t
T	Tt	Tt
t	tt	tt

34b. 50%

34c. 50%

34d. 0%

36. 12 in. by 12 in.

38. $\{z \mid z < 0.08\}$

40. $2x - 7y = -1$

42. about 18.26 amperes

Chapter 10 Using Factoring
10–1 Factors and Greatest Common Factors
Pages 561–563

1.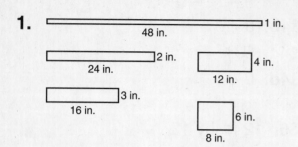

2. No; 4 is not prime.

3. No; the GCF of 4 and 9 is 1, but neither number is prime.

4. See students' work.

5. 1, 2, 4

6. 1, 2, 4, 7, 8, 14, 28, 56

7. prime

8. composite; $3 \cdot 13$

9. $-1 \cdot 2 \cdot 3 \cdot 5$

10. $2 \cdot 11 \cdot m \cdot m \cdot n$

11. 4

12. 5

13. $6d$

14. 1

15. $4gh$

16. $6a^2$

17. 40 in.

18. 1, 5, 25

19. 1, 67

20. 1, 2, 3, 4, 6, 9, 12, 18, 36

21. 1, 2, 4, 5, 8, 10, 16, 20, 40, 80

22. 1, 2, 4, 5, 8, 10, 16, 20, 25, 40, 50, 80, 100, 200, 400

23. 1, 5, 10, 19, 25, 38, 50, 95, 190, 950

24. prime

25. composite; $3^2 \cdot 7$

26. composite; $7 \cdot 13$

27. prime

28. composite; $2^4 \cdot 19$

29. composite; $2^2 \cdot 5 \cdot 7 \cdot 11$

30. $-1 \cdot 2 \cdot 5 \cdot 7$

31. $-1 \cdot 3 \cdot 3 \cdot 13$

32. $2 \cdot 3 \cdot 11 \cdot z \cdot z$

33. $2 \cdot 2 \cdot b \cdot b \cdot b \cdot d \cdot d$

34. $-1 \cdot 2 \cdot 3 \cdot 17 \cdot x \cdot x \cdot x \cdot y$

35. $-1 \cdot 2 \cdot 7 \cdot 7 \cdot a \cdot a \cdot b$

36. 18

37. 9

38. 12

39. 1

40. 17

41. 19

42. $17a$

43. $7pq$

44. $4a$

45. $15r^2t^2$

46. 6

47. 12

48. ab^2

49. 6

51. $8m^2n$

53. $-12x^3yz^2$

55. $3m^2n$

57. 29 cm by 47 cm

59. 3, 5; 5, 7; 11, 13; 17, 19; 29, 31; 41, 43; 59, 61; 71, 73

61a. $2b^3 \times 1 \times 1$
$2b^2 \times b \times 1$
$2b \times b \times b$
$b^3 \times 2 \times 1$
$b^2 \times 2b \times 1$
$b^2 \times 2 \times b$

61c. $4b^3 + 1$ or 865
$2b^3 + 2b^2 + 1$ or 505
$5b^2$ or 180
$3b^3 + 2$ or 650
$2b^3 + b^2 + b$ or 474
$b^3 + 2b^2 + 2b$ or 300

61d. Though the volume remains constant, the surface areas vary greatly.

63. 1500 squares of sod

65. $3b$

67.

```
←———⊕——⊕———→
 -1  0  1  2  3  4  5
```

69. $x = 4$

50. $2ab$

52. $6b^2c$

54. $6a^3b^2$

56. 1 in. by 116 in., 2 in. by 58 in., 4 in. by 29 in.

58. See students' work.

60a. 28

60b. 29

60c. 1

60d. 54

60e. 81

60f. 85

62. 5 rows of 20 plants, 10 rows of 10 plants, 20 rows of 5 plants

64. $1.21x^2 + 2.2xy + y^2$

66. (0, 0)

68. $x < 6$

70.

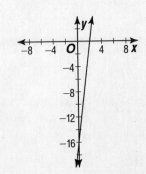

71. $9\frac{3}{5}$ feet

73. -4

72. 37.8 feet

74. the number z to the seventh power added to 2

10–2 Factoring Using the Distributive Property
Pages 568–571

1a. $2(4d^2 - 7d)$, $d(8d - 14)$, $2d(4d - 7)$

1b. $2d(4d - 7)$; $2d$ is the GCF of $8d^2$ and $14d$.

3. distributive, associative, commutative

5. $q - 7p^2$

7. 3

9. 1

11. $4xy^2$

13. $(a + b)(x + y)$

15. $(x - y)(3a + 4b)$

17. $3t$

19. $x(29y - 3)$

21. $3c^2d(1 - 2d)$

23. $(r + k)(x + 2y)$

25a. $g = \frac{1}{2}n(n - 1)$

25b. 91 games

25c. 63 games

27. $8rs$

29. $2y - 5$

31. $5k - 7p$

33. $2xz(7 - 9z)$

35. $a(17 - 41ab)$

37. $(m + x)(2y + 7)$

39. $3xy(x^2 + 3y + 12)$

41. $(2x^2 - 5y^2)(x - y)$

43. $(2x - 5y)(2a - 7b)$

45. $7abc(4abc + 3ac - 2)$

47. $2(2m + r)(3x - 2)$

49. $(7x + 3t - 4)(a + b)$

51. $8a - 4b + 8c + 16d + ab + 64$

2a. $ac + ad + bc + bd$

2b. $(a + b)(c + d)$

2c. They are equal.

4. $(4gh + 8h) + (3g + 6)$, $(4gh + 3g) + (8h + 6)$

6. $x(2x - 1)$

8. n

10. $3m$

12. $2xy$

14. $(3m + 5n)(a - 2b)$

16. $(x^2 + 1)(a^2 + b^2)$

18. $3x - 5y$

20. $x(x^4y - 1)$

22. $(a - c)(y - b)$

24. $(5a + 2b)(1 - 2a)$

26. $2g$

28. $11p$

30. $a + 3b$

32. $9t(t + 4)$

34. $y^3(15x + y)$

36. $(2x + b)(a + 3c)$

38. $(m^2 + p^2)(3 - 5p)$

40. $(a - 3b^2)(5a - 4b)$

42. $4x(3a + 5b + 8c)$

44. $(m - b)(3y + a)$

46. $3(2a - c)(a - b)$

48. $(x - 3y - z)(2a + b)$

50. $4(a + b + 4)$

52. $2r^2(4 - \pi)$

53. $4r^2(4 - \pi)$

55. $(4z + 3m)$ cm by $(z - 6)$ cm

57. Sample answer: $(3a + 2b)(ab + 6)$, $(3a + ab)(2b + 6)$, $(2b + ab)(3a + 6)$

59. $(2s - 3)(s + 8)$

61. A and C sharp

63. 9

65. $\{z \mid z \geq -1.654\}$

67. $\left\{(-3, 10), \left(0, \frac{11}{2}\right), (1, 4), \left(2, \frac{5}{2}\right), (5, -2)\right\}$

69. $y = -\frac{4}{3}x + \frac{7}{3}$

71. 7

54. $(5x - 6)$ cm by $(y + 3)$ cm

56. $(9x^2 + 30xy + 25y^2)$ in^2

58. $w(2w + 13)$ ft^2

60a. 144 m

60b. 9936 m^2

60c. $[w(w + 52)]$ m^2

60d. 8160 m^2

60e. Rugby Union

62a. about 70 people

62b. $886.38

64a.

64b. $148,000

66. $\left(6, \frac{1}{2}\right)$

68. 28

70. -10

1. So you do not waste time trying the same guess twice. It also helps you to make better guesses.

2. See students' work.

3a. It shows that the missing areas must have a sum of $8x$.

4. $(x + 4)(x - 1)$

3b. $(x + 6)(x + 2)$

5. 3, 8

6. $-5, 9$

7. 8, 5

8. $-1, -18$

9. $-2, -6$

10. $-15, 2$

11. $-$

12. 4

13. $(t + 3)(t + 4)$

14. $(c - 4)(c - 9)$

15. $2(y + 2)(y - 3)$

16. $3(d - 3)(d - 1)$

17. prime

18. $3(2p - 1)(p + 3)$

19. $9, -9, 15, -15$

20. $1, -1, 5, -5$

21. $(3x^2 + 2x)m^2$

22. $+$

23. $-$

24. $4y$

25. 5

26. $2x$

27. 5

28. $(b + 3)(b + 4)$

29. $(m - 4)(m - 10)$

30. $(z - 8)(z + 3)$

31. prime

32. $(s - 12)(s + 15)$

33. $(2x + 7)(x - 3)$

34. $(7a + 1)(a + 3)$

35. $(2x + 3)(x - 4)$

36. prime

37. $(2n - 7)(2n + 5)$

38. $2(9 - y)(4 - y)$

39. $(2 + 3m)(5 + 2m)$

40. $(a + 3b)(a - b)$

41. prime

42. $(5x - y)(3x - 2y)$

43. $2x(3x + 8)(2x - 5)$

44. $ab^2(5a - 9)(a + 4)$

45. $2a^2b(5a - 7b)(2a - 3b)$

46. $12, -12$

47. $7, -7, 11, -11$

48. $10, -10, 11, -11, 14, -14, 25, -25$

Algebra 1

49. 1, −1, 11, −11, 19, −19, 41, −41

50. 7, 12, 15, 16

51. 6, 4

52. 7 in²

53. r cm, $(5r + 6)$ cm, $(3r − 7)$ cm

54. yes

55. no; $(2x + 3)(x − 1)$

56. no; $(3x + 2)(x − 2)$

57. no; $(x − 3)(x − 3)$

58a. Sample answers:
16, $x^2 + 8x + 16 = (x + 4)(x + 4)$;
12, $x^2 + 8x + 12 = (x + 6)(x + 2)$;
7, $x^2 + 8x + 7 = (x + 7)(x + 1)$

58b. Sample answers:
9, $x^2 + 9x − 10 = (x + 10)(x − 1)$;
3, $x^2 + 3x − 10 = (x + 5)(x − 2)$;
−3, $x^2 + (−3)x − 10 = (x − 5)(x + 2)$

59. 27 ft³

60.

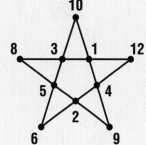

61. $(3x − 10)$ shares

62. 4

63. $(5, −2)$

64. {all numbers}

65. $y = -\frac{2}{3}x + \frac{14}{3}$

66. $-\frac{3}{2}$

67. D = {0, 1, 2}; R = {2, −2, 4}

68. 75%

69. 90°

70. Oct. 26 at 9:30 P.M.

71. $3x + 4y$

Self Test
Page 580

1. $10n^2$

2. $5a$

3. $6xy(3y − 4x)$

4. $(2a − 1)(b + m)$

5. $(2q + 3)(q − 6)$

6. prime

7. $(3y − 5)(y − 1)$

8. $3mn(9mn − 25)$

9. 41,312,432 or 23,421,314

10. $(x^2 + 17x + 66)$ m²

10–4 Factoring Differences of Squares
Pages 584–586

1. Each term of the binomial is a perfect square, and the binomial can be written as a difference of terms.

2. Sample answer: $a^2 - 25 = (a - 5)(a + 5)$

3. Write the binomial as a trinomial where the coefficient of the middle term is 0, and then factor this trinomial.

4. Patsy; if 7 is factored from each term, the binomial factor is the difference of squares $4f^2 - g^2$.

5. $\dfrac{15}{16} \cdot \dfrac{17}{16} =$

   $\dfrac{(16 - 1)(16 + 1)}{16^2} =$

   $\dfrac{16^2 - 1^2}{16^2} = \dfrac{255}{256}$

6. $(2 - x)(2 + x)$

7. yes

8. yes

9. no

10. c

11. d

12. b

13. a

14. $(t - 5)(t + 5)$

15. $(1 - 4g)(1 + 4g)$

16. prime

17. $5(2m - 3n)(2m + 3n)$

18. $(a + b - c)(a + b + c)$

19. $(x - y)(x + y)(x^2 + y^2)$

20. 391

21. 5

22. $(w - 9)(w + 9)$

23. $(2 - v)(2 + v)$

24. $(2q - 3)(2q + 3)$

25. $(10d - 1)(10d + 1)$

26. $(4a - 5b)(4a + 5b)$

27. $2(z - 7)(z + 7)$

28. $3(3g^2 - 25)$

29. prime

30. $2(2x - 3)(2x + 3)$

31. $17(1 - 2k)(1 + 2k)$

32. $(5y - 7z^2)(5y + 7z^2)$

33. prime

34. $(7h - 4)(7h + 4)$

35. prime

36. $9(3 - r)(3 + r)$

37. $(ax - 0.8y)(ax + 0.8y)$

38. $\left(\dfrac{1}{4}x + 5z\right)\left(\dfrac{1}{4}x - 5z\right)$

39. $\dfrac{1}{2}(3a - 7b)(3a + 7b)$

40. $(4p - 9q + 1)(4p - 9q - 1)$

41. $(a + b - c - d)(a + b + c + d)$

42. $(5x + 2y - 7z)(5x - 2y + 7z)$

43. $(x^2 - 2y)(x^2 + 2y)(x^4 + 4y^2)$

44. $a^2(a - b)(a + b)(a^2 + b^2)$

45. $(a^2 + 5b^2)(a - 2b)(a + 2b)$

46. 899

47. 624

48. 9964

49. $(2a - b)$ in., $(2a + b)$ in.

50. $(\pi r - 5\pi)$ cm, $(r + 5)$ cm or $(r - 5)$ cm, $(\pi r + 5\pi)$ cm

51. $(x - 2)$ ft, $(x + 4)$ ft

52. $(p - r)$ cm, $(p + r)$ cm, $(7m + 2n)$ cm

53. $(a - 5b)$ in., $(a + 5b)$ in., $(5a + 3b)$ in.

54.

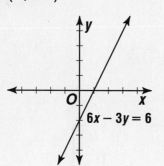

55a. square

55b. 25 cm²

56. 7, 24, 25

57. 9, 12, 15

58. $(2a + 1)(4a + 3)$

59. \$3.16, \$1.50, \$1.25, \$1.20

60. $3n^2 + 13n + 11$

61. (4, 16)

62. $\frac{15}{16}$

63.

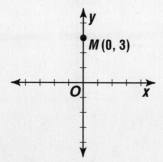

64. $b = 3a - 2$

65.

66. 0.471; 0.882; 0.533

67. 5.14, 3.6, 0.6

68a. $a + 10$

68b. $a + 1$

68c. no; $12 - 4 \neq 10$

10–5 Perfect Squares and Factoring
Pages 591–593

1a.

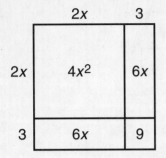

1b. It is a trinomial that can be represented by a square.

2a. See students' work.

2b. Sample answer: $x^2 + 2x + 1 = (x + 1)^2$

3a. Factor out the GCF of the terms.

3b. The other factoring patterns will be more apparent after the GCF has been factored out.

4. Samuel; $(a^2 - 1)$ can be factored as $(a - 1)(a + 1)$

5. Multiplying and factoring polynomials are inverse operations; see students' work.

6. 5

7. $8a$

8. $9n$

9. $6c$

10. yes; $(t + 9)^2$

11. yes; $(2n - 7)^2$

12. no

13. yes; $(4b - 7c)^2$

14. $5(3g^2 + 5)$

15. $4(a - 3b)(a + 3b)$

16. prime

17. $2(5g + 2)^2$

18. $3t(3t - 2)(t + 8)$

19. $(2a - 3b)(2a + 3b)(5x - y)$

20a. 16

20b.

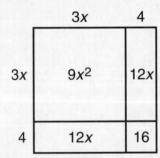

21. yes; $(r - 4)^2$

22. no

23. yes; $(7p - 2)^2$

24. yes; $(2y + 3z)^2$

25. no

26. no

27. yes; $(2m + n)^2$

28. yes; $(9t - 10)^2$

29. no

30. yes; $(10h + 1)^2$

31. no

32. yes; $(3a - 4)^2$

33. yes; $\left(\frac{1}{2}a + 3\right)^2$

34. yes; $\left(\frac{2}{3}x - 4\right)^2$

35. $a(45a - 32b)$

36. $(c - 3)(c - 2)$

37. $(v - 15)^2$

38. $(m - p^2)(m + p^2)$

39. prime

40. $3ab(a + 2 + 3b)$

41. $3(y - 7)(y + 7)$

42. $2(5n + 1)(2n + 3)$

43. $2(3a - 4)^2$

44. $3m(m + 8n)^2$

45. $(y^2 + z^2)(x - 1)(x + 1)$

46. prime

47. $(a^2 + 2)(4a + 3b^2)$

48. $(x + y - w + z)(x + y + w - z)$

49. $0.7(p - 3q)(p - 2q)$

50. $(x + 2y - 1)(x + 2y - 2)$

51. $(g^2 - 3h)(g + 3)^2$

52. $(4m - 5n)(3p + 2)(p - 2)$

53. $-110, 110$

54. y^2

55. 9

56. $-260, 260$

57. $(6y + 26)$ cm

58. $(x - 3y)$ in., $(x + 3y)$ in., $(xy + 7)$ in.

59. $(8x^2 - 22x + 14)$ cm²

60. 4 m

61a. $a \geq b$

61b. $a \leq b$

61c. $a = b$

63a. \$1166.40

64. $5(3x - 2yz)(3x + 2yz)$

63b. $p(1 + r)^2$

63c. \$1144.90

63d. See students' work.

65. $50.6t^2 + 21t - 102$

66. $12a^5$

67. 20 hours

68. $95° \leq F \leq 104°$

69a.

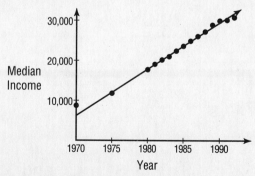

70. 30.7, 4.6

69b. Sample answer: Yes; $I =$ 1200y + 6000 where I is the median income and y is the number of years since 1970.

69c. See students' work.

71. 1:3

73. 152 ft

72. $b \approx \dfrac{70}{11}$, $c = \dfrac{30}{11}$

74. 4133 points

10–6 Solving Equations by Factoring
Pages 598–600

1. At least one of the factors equals 0.

2. equations that can be written as a product of factors that equal 0

3. No; the division would eliminate -3 as a solution.

4. Caitlin; the zero product property only works for 0. If you multiply two numbers and get 8, that does not mean that one of the numbers must have been 8.

5. $\{0, -5\}$

6. $\{-2, 4\}$

7. $\left\{0, \dfrac{5}{3}\right\}$

8. $\{-2, 7\}$

9. $\{5\}$

10. $\{0, 1, 28\}$

11. 6

12a. about 9.44 seconds

12b. about 356 feet

13. $\{0, 24\}$

14. $\{-4, 5\}$

15. $\left\{\dfrac{3}{2}, \dfrac{8}{3}\right\}$

16. $\left\{-\dfrac{5}{4}, \dfrac{7}{3}\right\}$

17. $\{-9, -4\}$

18. $\{-7, 8\}$

19. $\{-8, 8\}$

20. $\left\{0, \dfrac{5}{2}\right\}$

21. $\{0, 4\}$

22. $\{12\}$

23. $\left\{-\dfrac{1}{3}, -\dfrac{5}{2}\right\}$

24. $\left\{-7, 0, \dfrac{1}{5}\right\}$

25. $\{12, -4\}$

26. $\left\{-\dfrac{7}{3}, \dfrac{5}{2}\right\}$

27. $\{-9, 0, 9\}$

28. $\{-4, -5\}$

29. $\{-5, 7\}$

30. $\left\{-4, \dfrac{2}{3}\right\}$

31. -14 and -12 or 12 and 14

32. -33 and -31 or 31 and 33

33. 5 cm

34. $x^3 - 4x^2 - 21x = 0$

35a. $\{-6, 1\}$; $\{-6, 1\}$

36. 9 ft by 6 ft

35b. They are equivalent; they have the same solutions.

37a. about 3.35 s

37b. His ideas about falling objects differed from what most people thought to be true. He believed that Earth is a moving planet and that the sun and planets did not revolve around Earth.

39. about 90,180 ft or 17 mi

41. 0.5 km

43. $40q^2 + rq - 6r^2$

45. 14; −4

47. 4.355 minutes or about 4 minutes 21 seconds

38. Sample answer: Agree, since a nozzle speed of 215.16 ft/s should launch an object to a height of about 723 ft in a vacuum. Because of wind resistance, it may only go to 625 feet.

40. yes

42. $(10x + 1)^2$

44. $\left\{ x \mid x < \dfrac{3}{22} \right\}$

46.

s	4	2	0	−2	−4
$r(s)$	19	11	3	**−5**	**−13**

48. $700

Algebra 1

1. 630 ft

2. Sample answer: Once you determine the axis of symmetry, there is a matching point on the other side of the axis for each point you find on one side. Suppose the axis is $x = 4$ and one point is $(-2, 3)$. -2 is 6 units left of the axis; another point is 6 units right of the axis with the same y-coordinate, that is, $(10, 3)$.

3. If (p, q) is the vertex, $x = p$ is the equation of the axis of symmetry.

4. Angie is correct. The graph of $y = (-x)^2$ is the same graph as $y = x^2$, which opens upward from the origin. The graph of $y = -x^2$ opens downward from the origin.

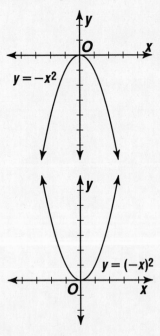

Algebra 1

5. If the coefficient of x^2 is positive, it is a minimum. If the coefficient is negative, it is a maximum.

6. It opens downward; $x = 2$.

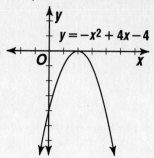

$y = -x^2 + 4x - 4$

7. $x = 0$, $(0, 2)$, minimum

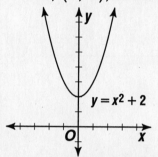

$y = x^2 + 2$

8. $x = 0$, $(0, 0)$, maximum

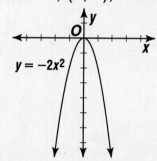

$y = -2x^2$

9. $x = -2$, $(-2, -13)$, minimum

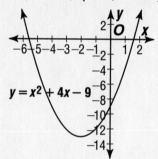

$y = x^2 + 4x - 9$

10. $x = 7$, $(7, -13)$, minimum

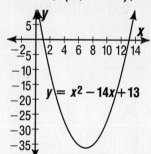

$y = x^2 - 14x + 13$

11. $x = 2.5$, $(2.5, 12.25)$, maximum

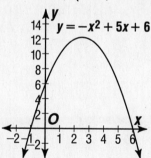

$y = -x^2 + 5x + 6$

12. $x = 1$, $(1, 8.5)$, maximum

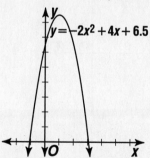

$y = -2x^2 + 4x + 6.5$

13. c

14a. about 1.25s

14b. 28 ft

15. $x = 0$, $(0, 0)$, minimum

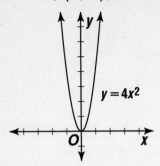

$y = 4x^2$

16. $x = 2$, $(2, 3)$, maximum

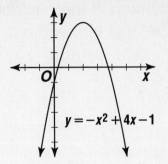

$y = -x^2 + 4x - 1$

17. $x = -1$, $(-1, 17)$, minimum

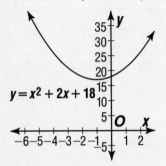

$y = x^2 + 2x + 18$

18. $x = \frac{3}{2}$, $\left(\frac{3}{2}, -\frac{49}{4}\right)$, minimum

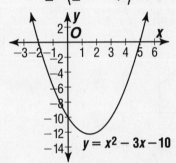

$y = x^2 - 3x - 10$

19. $x = 0$, $(0, -5)$, minimum

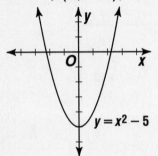

$y = x^2 - 5$

20. $x = 0$, $(0, 16)$, minimum

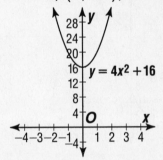

$y = 4x^2 + 16$

21. $x = -3$, $(-3, -29)$, minimum

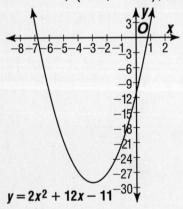

$y = 2x^2 + 12x - 11$

22. $x = -4$, $(-4, 32)$, minimum

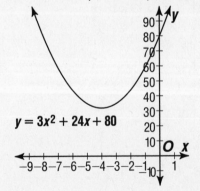

$y = 3x^2 + 24x + 80$

23. $x = 0$, $(0, -25)$, minimum

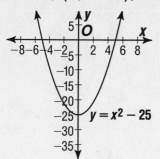

$y = x^2 - 25$

24. $x = -3$, $(-3, 24)$, maximum

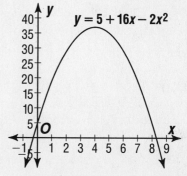

$y = 15 - 6x - x^2$

25. $x = 4$, $(4, 37)$, maximum

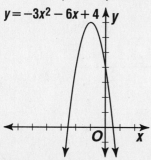

$y = -3x^2 - 6x + 4$

26. $x = -1$, $(-1, 7)$, maximum

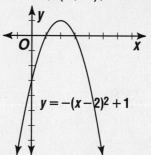

$y = 5 + 16x - 2x^2$

27. $x = -1$, $(-1, -20)$, minimum

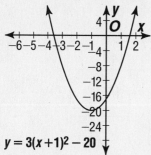

$y = 3(x+1)^2 - 20$

28. $x = 2$, $(2, 1)$, maximum

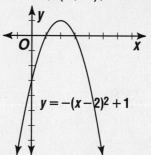

$y = -(x-2)^2 + 1$

29. $x = -1$, $(-1, -1)$, minimum

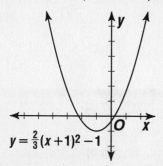

$y = \frac{2}{3}(x+1)^2 - 1$

30. b

31. c

32. a

Algebra 1

33.

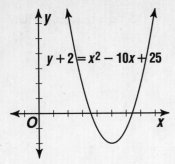

$y + 2 = x^2 - 10x + 25$

34.

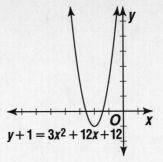

$y + 1 = 3x^2 + 12x + 12$

35.

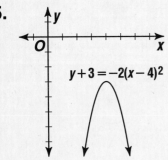

$y + 3 = -2(x - 4)^2$

36.

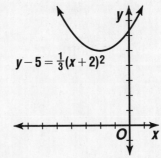

$y - 5 = \frac{1}{3}(x + 2)^2$

37. $x = -1$

38. 3

39. $x = 2$

40. $(-2.00, 12)$

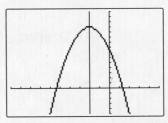

41. $(-1.10, 125.8)$

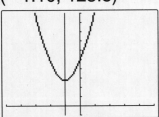

42. $(-268.04, -1719.47)$

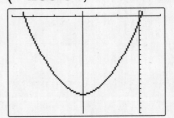

43. $(-0.15, 90.14)$

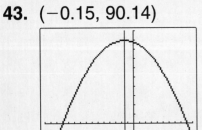

44. $(-3, 11), (2, 6)$; See students' work.

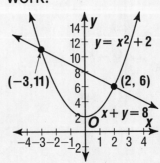

Algebra 1

45a.

Year	t	$U(t)$
1970	0	329.96
1975	5	370.31
1980	10	559.16
1985	15	896.51
1990	20	1382.36
1995	23	1745.15

45b. D : $0 \leq t \leq 23$;
R : $326 < U(t) < 1746$

45c.

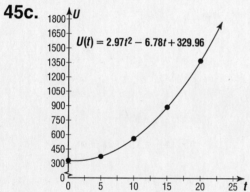

$U(t) = 2.97t^2 - 6.78t + 329.96$

45d. See students' work.

47. 0.15 km

49a. 6790 km

49b. 2.2792×10^8 km

51a.

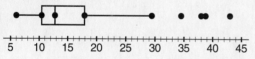

51b. 34.5, 38, 38.7, 43

46a. $H(t) = 80t - 16t^2 + 2$

46b. 66 ft, 98 ft, 98 ft

46c. about 5 seconds

48. $x^2 - 12x + 32$

50. $(-3, -4)$

52.

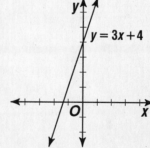

$y = 3x + 4$

53. -5

54. 48, 96

11–2 Solving Quadratic Equations by Graphing
Pages 624–627

1. The *x*-intercept is where the function equals 0.

2. Hanna, because factoring only works when the polynomial making up the equation is factorable. Graphing will always give you an estimate of the solutions if they are real.

3. $f(x) = x^2 + 6x + 6$

4. 500 employees

5. See students' work.

6. 1 distinct root

7. 2 real roots

8. no real roots ($\varnothing$)

9. $-1, 2$

10. 1, 6
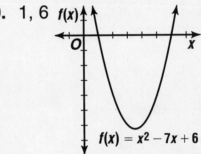
$f(x) = x^2 - 7x + 6$

11. $-3, 8$
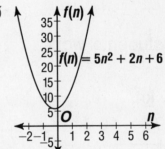
$f(c) = c^2 - 5c - 24$

12. $\varnothing$
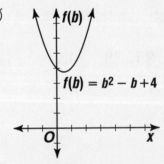
$f(n) = 5n^2 + 2n + 6$

13. $-2 < w < -1, 4 < w < 5$

$f(w) = w^2 - 3w - 5$

14. $\varnothing$

$f(b) = b^2 - b + 4$

15. 5

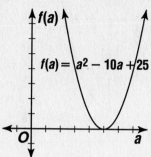

$f(a) = a^2 - 10a + 25$

16. 8 and −3
17. −2, −6
18. −2, 2
19. 2
20. −3, −4

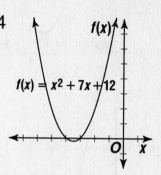

$f(x) = x^2 + 7x + 12$

21. −4, 4

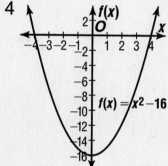

$f(x) = x^2 - 16$

22. $-5 < x < -4, \; -2 < a < -1$

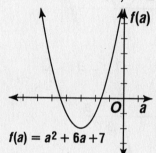

$f(a) = a^2 + 6a + 7$

23. −3

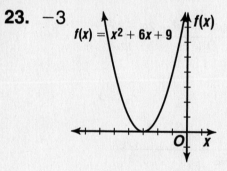

$f(x) = x^2 + 6x + 9$

24. −6, 2

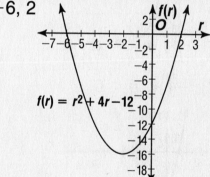

$f(r) = r^2 + 4r - 12$

25. ∅

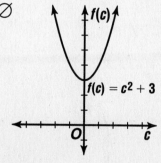

$f(c) = c^2 + 3$

26. −8, −2

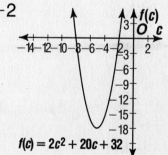

$f(c) = 2c^2 + 20c + 32$

27. −4, 1

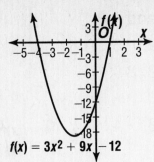

$f(x) = 3x^2 + 9x - 12$

28. −3, 3

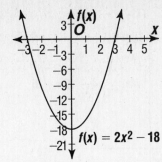

$f(x) = 2x^2 - 18$

29. 4

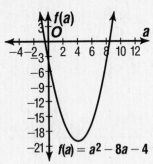

$f(p) = p^2 - 8p + 16$

30. 3, 7

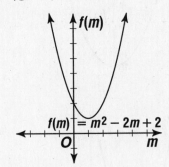

$f(w) = w^2 - 10w + 21$

31. $8 < a < 9, -1 < a < 0$

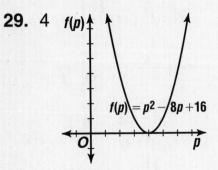

$f(a) = a^2 - 8a - 4$

32. ∅

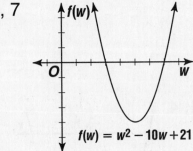

$f(m) = m^2 - 2m + 2$

33. $3, -1 < n < 0$

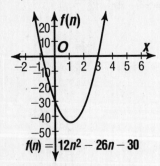

$f(n) = 12n^2 - 26n - 30$

34. $-4 < x < -3, 2 < x < 3$

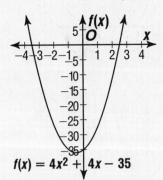

$f(x) = 4x^2 + 4x - 35$

35.

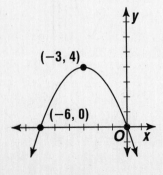

(−3, 4)

(−6, 0)

36.

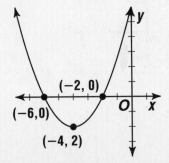

(−2, 0)

(−6, 0)

(−4, 2)

37.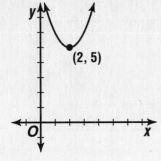

(2, 5)

38.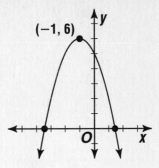

(−1, 6)

39. −4, −8 or 4, 8

40. 4, 5

41. no solution

42. 9 and 7 or −9 and −7

43. −2, −6

44. $0 < y < 1, 3 < y < 4$

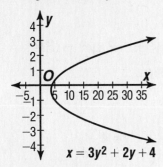

$x = -0.75y^2 - 6y - 9$

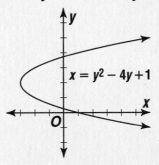

$x = y^2 - 4y + 1$

45. no y-intercepts

46. −1.66, 1.66

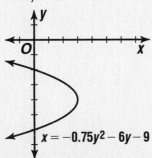

$x = 3y^2 + 2y + 4$

47. no real roots

48. −11

49. 0.29, 1.71

50. −1.6, 0.85

51. −0.79, 2.54

52a. 2.25

52b. $k < 2.25$

52c. $k > 2.25$

53a. −2

53b. $k > -2$

53c. $k < -2$

54. The value of the function changes from negative to positive as it moves from $x = 10$ to $x = 11$. In order to do this, it must cross the x-axis between 10 and 11. Therefore, an x-intercept occurs between 10 and 11. Thus, the root of the related equation lies between 10 and 11.

55a. $f(x) = -x^2 - 4x + 12$

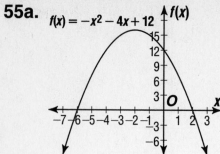

55b. 8 feet

55c. 16 feet

55d. $85\frac{1}{3}$ ft^2

55e. $297

57. $x = 0$; $(0, 4)$

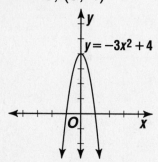

59. $(4x - 3)$ m by $(2x - 1)$ m

61. 6

63. $-4 < x < \frac{4}{3}$

65. $24.75

56a.

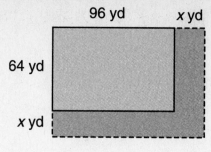

56b. $x^2 + 160x - 1644 = 0$

56c. 32 yards

56d. 96×128 yards

58. $\left\{0, -\frac{2}{9}\right\}$

60. $x^3 - 6x^2y + 12xy^2 - 8y^3$

62. no solution

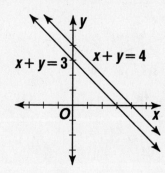

64.

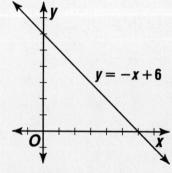

66. 0

11–3 Solving Quadratic Equations by Using the Quadratic Formula
Pages 631–633

1. Evaluate the formula using + for one root; then reevaluate using − for the other.

2. You get the square root of a negative number.

3a. 102.05 million

3b. 113.23 million

4. See students' work.

5. 1, 3, −18; 3, −6

6. −1, −5, −2; −4.56, −0.44

7. 4, −2, 15; no real roots

8. 1, 0, −25; ±5

9. 1.83, −2.33

10. ∅

11. −1, −6

12. −2.12, 15.12

13. about 29.4 ft/s

14. −4, 6

15. −8.61, −1.39

16. −10, −2

17. $-\frac{4}{5}$, 1

18. ∅

19. $-\frac{5}{3}$, 4

20. −6

21. −2.91, 2.41

22. −5, 3

23. 7

24. −0.29, 0.87

25. $-\frac{3}{2}$, $-\frac{5}{3}$

26. −2, 2

27. −6, 6

28. ∅

29. $-\frac{1}{3}$, 1

30. $-\frac{3}{4}$, $\frac{5}{6}$

31. −3, $-\frac{1}{2}$

32. $\frac{2}{5}$, $\frac{1}{5}$

33. 0.60, −0.25

34. −0.28, 0.90

35. 0.5, 2

36. 0.6, 1.6

37. −0.2, 1.4

38. 1, 2, −2; $x^2 + 2x − 2 = 0$

39. 4, 20, 23; $4x^2 + 20x + 23 = 0$

40. 1, −4, $-\frac{13}{4}$; $x^2 − 4x − \frac{13}{4} = 0$

41a. 10, 1

41b. none

41c. −0.5

41d. −1, 0.7142857143

42.

Equation	$x^2 - 4x + 1 = 0$	$x^2 + 6x + 11 = 0$	$x^2 - 4x + 4 = 0$
Value of the Discriminant	12	−8	0
Graph of the Equation	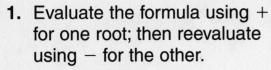		
Number of x-intercepts	2	none	1
Number of y-intercepts	2	none	1 distinct root

43a. Discriminant is not a perfect square.

43b. Discriminant is a perfect square, but the expression is not an integer.

43c. Discriminant is a perfect square, and the equation can be factored.

43d. Discriminant is 0, and the equation is a perfect square.

45a. Y, 10 mg; C, 8.75 mg

45b. $0 = a^2 - 11a + 12$; 1.2 yr, 9.8 yr

44a. $D : 0 \le t \le 13$; $R : 511.4 \le l(t) < 1205$

44b. \$1204.6 billion

44c. \$1614.2 billion

44d. 1989

46. $-7, -3$

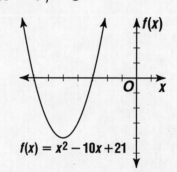

$f(x) = x^2 - 10x + 21$

47. $\{0, -9\}$

49. 24, 18

51. yes

53. $-4°F$

48. $21a^3 - 6a^2 - 46a + 28$

50.

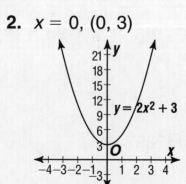

52. -12

Self Test
Page 633

1. $x = \dfrac{1}{2}, \left(\dfrac{1}{2}, -\dfrac{25}{4}\right)$

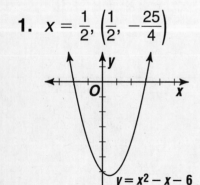

$y = x^2 - x - 6$

2. $x = 0, (0, 3)$

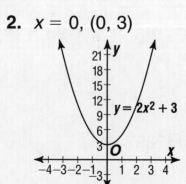

$y = 2x^2 + 3$

3. $x = 0$, $(0, 7)$

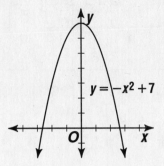

$y = -x^2 + 7$

4a. 72.5 s

4b. 0 seconds; this is the maximum height.

5. -9, 9

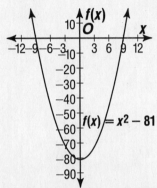

$f(x) = x^2 - 81$

6. $2 < x < 3$, $-4 < x < -3$

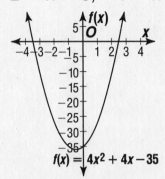

$f(x) = 4x^2 + 4x - 35$

7. $\varnothing$

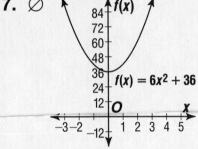

$f(x) = 6x^2 + 36$

8. -6, -1

9. $\varnothing$

10. -2.12, 15.12

11–4 Exponential Functions
Pages 640–642

1a. $1.844674407 \times 10^{19}$

1b. over 3.8×10^{11} tons

2a. No, it does not.

2b. Sample answer: Use the graph of $y = 2^x$ and the TRACE feature on a graphing calculator to examine the y values.

2c. no; only those of the form $y = a^x$

3a. No, it does not.

3b. See students' work.

4. If $a = 1$, $a^x = 1$ for any value of x.

3c. Yes.

5. See students' work.

7. 5.20

9. 12.51

6a.

Fold	1	2	3	4	5	6
Area	$\frac{1}{2}$	$\frac{1}{4}$	$\frac{1}{8}$	$\frac{1}{16}$	$\frac{1}{32}$	$\frac{1}{64}$

6b. Each fold makes a rectangle whose area is $\frac{1}{2^x}$, where x is the number of folds.

6c. $y = 0.5^x$

8. 0.37

10. 1

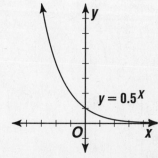

11. 7

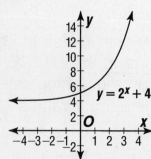

12. Yes, increases by a factor of 6.

13. −2

15. −2

17. 10.56

19. 1.63

21. 25.86

23. 0.86

25. 5

14. 3

16. 3.32 hours

18. 0.32

20. 0.01

22. 1.38

24. 844.49

26. 16

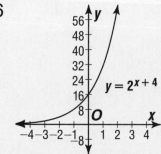

27. 3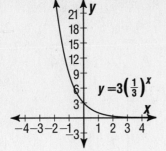

28. 2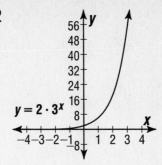

29. 1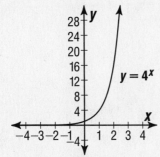

30. 1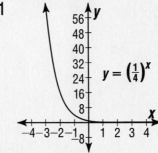

31. no, linear

32. yes, constant factor

33. no, no pattern

34. −1

35. −7

36. −0.5

37. −3

38. $-\frac{3}{2}$

39. 3

40. −2

41. 3, −1

42. −1, −3

43. All have the same shape but different *y*-intercepts.

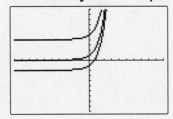

44. All have the same shape but different *y*-intercepts.

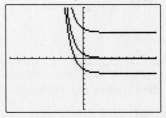

45. All have the same shape but are positioned at different places along the *x*-axis.

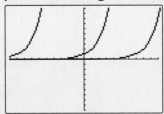

46. All have the same *y*-intercept, but each rises more steeply than the previous one.

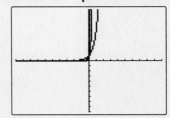

47a. 2.51

47b. You cannot write 10 as a power or 2.5.

48a. 0

48b. 0

48c. −7

51. $-3, -\dfrac{1}{2}$

53. $\dfrac{1}{5}ab(4a - 3b - 1)$

55. 184

48d. c

48e. c

52a. $(4p - 5r)$ km by $(4p - 5r)$ km

52b.

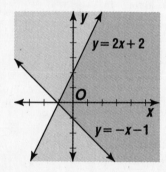

54. 8 miles

56.

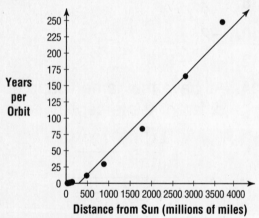

57a–b.

57b. Sample answer:
$y = 0.07x - 12$

57c. 275 years

59. 60

58. 75 m

11–5 Growth and Decay
Pages 646–649

1a. California

1b. CA: 34.02 million;
NE: 1.70 million

3a. 1

3b. 2

3c. 4

3d. 365

5. decay

7. about $70,000,000,000

9. $661.44

11. $10,962.19

13a. Each equation represents growth and t is the number of years since 1994.
$y = 58.7(1.025)^t$
$y = 919.9(1.019)^t$
$y = 35.6(1.021)^t$
$y = 2.9(1.013)^t$

13b. 68.1 million, 1029.9 million, 40.3 million, 3.1 million

13c.

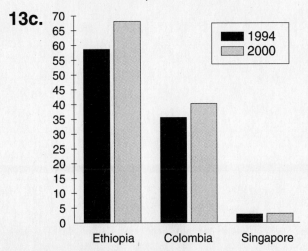

15a. $y = 231.5(1.0963)^t$, $t =$ years since 1950, growth

15b. 57.6 trillion

2. The 7% graph would rise more steeply than the 0.7% graph when using the same scale.

4. growth

6. decay

8. about 7 years

10. $2097.86

12. $15,121.61

14a. $y = 114.6(0.934)^t$, $t =$ years since 1950, decay

14b. It never reaches 0, but comes close in about 100 years.

16a. $y = 1.2(0.932)^t$, $t =$ number of years since 1980, decay

16b. 1990

16c. preservation efforts, conservation of lands, domestic reproduction in zoos, poaching

16d. daily

17a. $6931.53

17b. $6954.58

17c. $23.05

17d. daily

18. 97.5 MHz

19a–c. See students' work.

20a. 20 years

20b. -0.0693

21. $a > 1$, growth; $0 < a < 1$, decay; x represents time

22. The y-intercept is C.

23. $-\dfrac{1}{2}$

24. $-n^2 - 3n - 5$

25. $-\dfrac{r^{10}t^2}{3}$

26. $y^3 z^{12}$

27. $-2.5x + 2$

Chapter 12   Exploring Rational Expressions and Equations
12–1 Simplifying Rational Expressions
Pages 663–665

1. When $x = 2$, the denominator becomes zero. Division by zero is undefined.

2. about 3

3. Factor the denominator, set each of its factors equal to zero, and solve for x. This will tell you that the restricted values are -5 and -1.

4. Sample answer: $\dfrac{x-2}{(x+2)(x-7)}$

5. The multiplication effect of using a tool or lever to carry out a task.

6. $a; \dfrac{13}{14y}; a \neq 0, y \neq 0$

7. $7a^2b; \dfrac{-b^2}{3a^3}; a \neq 0, b \neq 0$

8. $a; \dfrac{m+3}{m-2}; m \neq 2, a \neq 0$

9. $b; \dfrac{3}{b+5}; b \neq 0, b \neq -5$

10. $r - s; \dfrac{r+s}{r-s}; r - s \neq 0$

11. $m - 3; \dfrac{1}{m+3}; m \neq \pm 3$

12. 6

13a. 5

13b. 750 lb

14. $\dfrac{5}{13a}; a \neq 0$

15. $\dfrac{5y}{2x}; y \neq 0, z \neq 0$

16. $\dfrac{4a}{7b}; a \neq 0, b \neq 0$

17. $\dfrac{4}{5x}; x \neq 0, y \neq 0$

18. $\dfrac{4}{3+a}; a \neq -3$ or 0

19. $y; y \neq -\dfrac{1}{3}$

20. $\dfrac{x-3}{2}; x \neq -3$

21. $y + 7x; y \neq 7x$

22. $\dfrac{1}{x-4}; x \neq -5$ or 4

23. $\dfrac{1}{a-4}; a \neq 3$ or 4

24. $\dfrac{3}{x-2}; x \neq 2$ or 5

25. $\dfrac{1}{x+4}; x \neq -4$

26. $\dfrac{x-5}{x-4}; x \neq 4$ or -3

27. $\dfrac{a+6}{a+4}; a \neq -4$ or 2

28. $\dfrac{x-6}{x-5}; x \neq -6$ or 5

29. $\dfrac{b+1}{b-9}; b \neq 9$ or 4

30. $\dfrac{7}{6}; x \neq -1.5$ or -1

31. $\dfrac{4}{5}; x \neq -1$

32. $-\dfrac{4}{3}$

33. $-\dfrac{5}{3}$

34. $\dfrac{1}{5}$

35. not possible, $y \neq -2$

36. Because $m \neq -4$ in the original expression.

37a. 192

37b. 3840 lb

39a. 9.5°/mile

39b. $-\dfrac{95}{10} = -\dfrac{19}{2}$

39c.

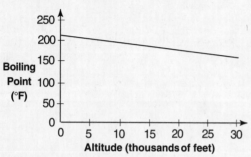

38a. 6.79 lb/in²

38b. 2.83 lb/in²

38c. no, 3.96 lb/in²

40. $7302.90

41. ±11

42. $-15x^3 - 6x^2 + 21x$

43.

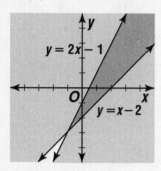

44. {8, −8}

45.

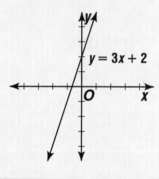

46. −4

12–2 Multiplying Rational Expressions
Pages 668–670

1. $\dfrac{x}{x-4}$, y

2. Angie; she divided out the GCF.

3. See students' work.

4. $\dfrac{12m}{5}$

5. $\dfrac{9m}{2xy}$

6. $\dfrac{r}{y+3}$

7. $\dfrac{4}{x+3}$

8. $3(a+5)$

9. $\dfrac{4}{3}$

11a. 91.44 cm/yd

11b. changing centimeters to yards

13. $\dfrac{3a}{2}$

15. $\dfrac{2}{x}$

17. $8y$

19. $\dfrac{4m}{3(m+5)}$

21. $\dfrac{2m}{a+9}$

23. 2

25. $3(x-y)$

27. 36

29. $\dfrac{4x}{3x-5}$

31. $\dfrac{4}{5(x+5)}$

33. 21.8 mph; converts ft/s to mph

35. 10,800 Calories

37. Sample answer:

$\dfrac{3(x+2)}{x+7} \cdot \dfrac{2(x-3)}{x-4}$,

$\dfrac{6}{x+7} \cdot \dfrac{x^2-x-1}{x-4}$

39a. $\dfrac{1 \text{ franc}}{0.1981 \text{ dollars}} \cdot \dfrac{1 \text{ dollar}}{5.05 \text{ francs}}$

39b. 12,500 pesos ·

$\dfrac{0.1597 \text{ dollars}}{1 \text{ peso}} \cdot \dfrac{1 \text{ franc}}{0.1981 \text{ dollars}}$,
about 10,077 francs

39c. Convert to American dollars and then to Hong Kong's dollar.

41. 729

43. 4

45. 0

10. $\dfrac{x+3}{3(x+1)}$

12. yes; $\dfrac{20 \text{ mi}}{1 \text{ h}} \cdot \dfrac{5280 \text{ ft}}{1 \text{ mi}} \cdot \dfrac{1 \text{ h}}{60 \text{ min}}$

14. $3m^2$

16. $\dfrac{4b^2r}{3a}$

18. $\dfrac{5ac}{3}$

20. $\dfrac{7(a+2b)(m+5)}{a+b}$

22. $3(r+3)$

24. $\dfrac{16}{a+1}$

26. $\dfrac{3a}{a-3}$

28. 3

30. $b+1$

32. $\dfrac{a+4}{a+2}$

34. 20 yd³; converts ft³ to yd³

36. 40.25 grams

38a. $\dfrac{24 \text{ s}}{1 \text{ car}} \cdot \dfrac{6864 \text{ cars}}{8 \text{ collectors}} \cdot$
$\dfrac{1 \text{ min}}{60 \text{ s}} \cdot \dfrac{1 \text{ h}}{60 \text{ min}}$

38b. 20,592 seconds = 5.72 hours

40a. 4.5

40b. about 29 minutes

40c. about 41 minutes

40d. The times are not doubled; the difference is 12 minutes.

42. -3

44. $(-2, -3)$

46. $705

1. The wrong reciprocal was used.

2. $\dfrac{10}{d}, \dfrac{d}{r}$

3. See students' work.

4. $\dfrac{3}{m^2}$

5. $\dfrac{5}{x}$

6. $\dfrac{4y}{-9}$

7. $\dfrac{y+3}{x^2-9}$

8. $\dfrac{1}{m-3}$

9. $\dfrac{1}{x^2+2x+5}$

10. $\dfrac{x}{x-5}$

11. $\dfrac{(m+2)^2}{4}$

12. $\dfrac{5}{a+5}$

13. $\dfrac{x+4}{x+6}$

14. 10.7 cubic yards

15. 0.5 ft³

16a. $\dfrac{40\text{ mi}}{1\text{ h}} \cdot \dfrac{5280\text{ ft}}{1\text{ mi}} \cdot \dfrac{1\text{ h}}{60\text{ min}} \cdot \dfrac{1\text{ car}}{48\text{ ft}}$

16b. $73\dfrac{1}{3}$ cars

17. $\dfrac{a}{a+11}$

18. $\dfrac{m+3}{m}$

19. $\dfrac{b^2m}{c^2}$

20. $\dfrac{3}{2x}$

21. $\dfrac{m+5}{m}$

22. $\dfrac{3x}{(x+2)(x-1)}$

23. $\dfrac{4}{z+3}$

24. $\dfrac{1}{(x+2)(x+1)}$

25. $\dfrac{2(x+5)}{x+1}$

26. $\dfrac{1}{2(m+2)}$

27. $x+3$

28. $\dfrac{1}{(m+7)(m+1)}$

29. $x+5$

30. $\dfrac{m+4}{m+1}$

31. $(x+5)(x+3)$

32. $(t+2)(w-4)$

33. 88 ft/s; Sample answer: changes 60 mph to ft/s

34. 13,062.5 in.; Sample answer: calculates how far a needle travels on a record for a song 16.5 minutes long

35. 27.5 yd³; changes ft³ to yd³

36. 16.7 meters/s; changes 60 km/h to m/s

37. $\dfrac{x-y}{4}$

38a. $\left[\dfrac{5\text{ ft }(18\text{ ft}+15\text{ ft})}{2} \cdot 9\text{ft} \right] \div \dfrac{27\text{ ft}^3}{1\text{ yd}^3}$

38b. $727.\overline{27}$ truckloads

39a. 5500 miles

39b. 41.3 trains

39c. 10,618.2 miles; 27.3 trains

41. $\dfrac{8}{m-5}$

40a. $\dfrac{\dfrac{2\pi\left(3\frac{3}{4}\text{ in.}\right)}{1\text{ revolution}} \cdot \dfrac{33\frac{1}{3}\text{ revolutions}}{1\text{ minute}}}{\dfrac{16.5\text{ minutes}}{1}}$ ·

40b. about 1079.92 ft

42. $-4, -2$

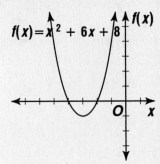

43. $(4a - 3b^2)^2$

45. $x < -2$

47. $7 + 2 = 2 + 7$

44. 2.46×10^9

46. -9

12–4 Dividing Polynomials
Pages 678–680

1. dividend, $2x^2 - 11x - 20$; divisor, $2x + 3$; quotient, $x - 7 + \dfrac{1}{2x + 3}$

3. 3 rolls

2. It means the divisor goes evenly into the dividend or it is a factor of the dividend.

4a. $(2x - 3)(x - 3)$

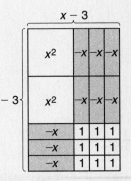

4b. $x - 3; 2x - 3$

6. $\dfrac{a}{5} + 1 + \dfrac{13}{5a}$

8. $s + 9$

10. $3r - 4 + \dfrac{27}{r + 5}$

12. $\dfrac{x^2}{2} + x - \dfrac{5}{2x}$

14. $a + 2 + \dfrac{2}{3a}$

5. $3b^2 - 5$

7. $t - 1$

9. $2m + 3 + \dfrac{-3}{m + 2}$

11. $(2x + 3)$ meters

13. $\dfrac{b}{3} + 3 - \dfrac{7}{3b}$

15. $\dfrac{m}{7} + 1 - \dfrac{4}{m}$

16. $3y - 5 + \dfrac{1}{xy}$

17. $a^2 + 2a + 12 + \dfrac{3}{a - 2}$

18. $b + 2 - \dfrac{3}{2b - 1}$

19. $m - 3 - \dfrac{2}{m + 7}$

20. $x - 5 - \dfrac{1}{2x + 3}$

21. $2x + 6 + \dfrac{1}{x - 7}$

22. $2 + \dfrac{5}{a} + \dfrac{2}{7b^2}$

23. $3m^2 + 4k^2 - 2$

24. $3r + 2 - \dfrac{1}{r + 6}$

25. $a + 7 - \dfrac{1}{a + 3}$

26. $2m - 3 + \dfrac{2}{2m + 7}$

27. $3x - 2 + \dfrac{21}{2x + 3}$

28. $y - 15 - \dfrac{51}{y - 4}$

29. $t + 4 - \dfrac{5}{4t + 1}$

30. $x + 6 + \dfrac{-3}{x + 3}$

31. $8x^2 + \dfrac{32x}{7} - 9$

32a. $7x - 9 + \dfrac{15}{x + 2}$

32b. $\dfrac{1}{3}x - \dfrac{46}{9} - \dfrac{4\frac{5}{9}}{3x + 4}$

33a. $x^2 + 4x + 4$

34. 63

33b. $5t^2 - 3t - 2$

33c. $2a^2 + 3a - 4$

35. -15

36. 27

37. \$480,000

38a.

Material	Density
aluminum	2.7
gold	19.3
silver	10.5
steel	7.8
iron	7.8
copper	8.9
blood	1.1
lead	11.3
brass	8.6
concrete	2.0

38b.

```
 x x x            x x    x                              x
                  x x    x
 1 2 3 4 5 6 7 8 9 10 11 12 13 14 15 16 17 18 19
```

38c. The data's density is clustered around 9.

39. $-\dfrac{x}{7}$

40.

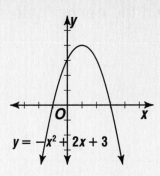

$y = -x^2 + 2x + 3$

41. $3(x - 7)(x + 5)$

42. $(2x^2 + 3xy + y^2)$ units^2

43. $(1, 3)$

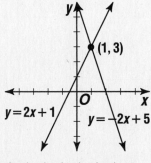

$y = 2x + 1$ $y = -2x + 5$

44. $y = 2x$

45.

-3 -2 -1 0 1 2 3 4 5 6

Self Test
Page 680

1. $\dfrac{25x}{36y}$

2. already simplified

3. $\dfrac{(x + 4)(4x^2 + 2x - 3)}{(x + 3)(x + 2)(x - 1)}$

4. $\dfrac{x - 1}{x + 5}$

5. $\dfrac{x - 5}{x + 4}$

6. $\dfrac{x + 5}{x - 5}$

7. $(2x - 5)$

8. $3x + \dfrac{-4}{x - 2}$

9. $4(3x - 1)$ or $(12x - 4)$ units

10. 330 miles

12–5 Rational Expressions with Like Denominators
Pages 683–684

1. The two expressions whose sum is zero have opposite signs but equal absolute values, and the two expressions whose difference is zero are equal and have the same sign.

2. Combine the numerators, use their like denominator, and simplify.

3. She added the denominators.

4. x

5. $\dfrac{10}{x}$

6. $\dfrac{1}{m}$

7. $\dfrac{10}{a + 2}$

8. 2

9. 3

10. $3x$

11. m

12. $-\dfrac{5y}{11}$

13. $-\dfrac{a}{6}$

14. $-\dfrac{1}{z}$

15. 2

16. 1

17. $\dfrac{7}{x + 7}$

18. 2

19. 1

20. $\dfrac{4m + 5}{2m + 3}$

21. 1

22. 3

23. $\dfrac{4x}{x + 2}$

24. 2

25. $\dfrac{2y - 6}{y + 3}$

26. $\dfrac{3m - 5}{m - 2}$

27. 2

28. $\dfrac{6t + 2}{1 - 4t}$

29. $\dfrac{25x - 93}{2x + 5}$

30. $\dfrac{b - 7}{2b + 12}$

31. $\dfrac{24x + 26y}{7x - 2y}$

32. 4

33. b

34a. 6.657 gallons

34b. 296,938,414,100 gallons

35. 442 days

36. 1680.7

37. $\pm\dfrac{6}{5}$

38. $2x^2 + 8y + 4x + 4$

39. $-3, 4$

40.

41. $\dfrac{1}{216}$

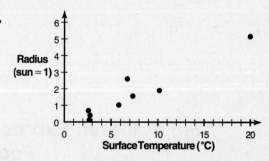

Algebra 1

12–6 Rational Expressions with Unlike Denominators
Pages 687–689

1. Yes; no; no common factors were divided.

2. $\frac{3x}{4} + \frac{7}{8x}$; $8x$ is the LCD.

3. x^2

4. a^2b^2

5. $90m^2b^2$

6. $(a + 6)(a + 7)$

7. $(x - 3)(x + 3)$

8. $2(x - 4)$

9. $\frac{7 + 9m}{15m^2}$

10. $\frac{5x + 5}{(x + 3)(x - 2)}$

11. $\frac{3(x^2 + 4x + 1)}{x + 2}$

12. $\frac{-5m - 4}{(m + 3)(m + 1)}$

13. $\frac{22 - 7y}{6y^2}$

14. $\frac{22g - 31}{(2g - 7)(3g + 1)}$

15. 168 members

16. $\frac{17m}{20}$

17. $\frac{-5x}{63}$

18. $\frac{4}{3}$

19. $\frac{7yz + 3}{xyz}$

20. $\frac{7 - 10a}{6a^2}$

21. $\frac{2s - 3t}{s^2t^2}$

22. $\frac{15m + 28}{35m^2}$

23. $\frac{7z + 8}{(z + 5)(z - 4)}$

24. $\frac{d^2 + 6d + 12}{(d + 4)(d + 3)}$

25. $\frac{k^2 + k - 10}{(k + 5)(k + 3)}$

26. $\frac{-y^2 + 6y + 12}{(y - 3)(y + 4)}$

27. $\frac{-17r - 32}{(3r - 2)(r - 5)}$

28. $\frac{3a^2 - 2a + 8}{3(a - 2)(a + 2)}$

29. $\frac{10 + m}{2(2m - 3)}$

30. $\frac{1}{3}$

31. $\frac{3w - 4}{3(5w + 2)}$

32. $\frac{h^2 + h - 6}{(h + 2)^2}$

33. $\frac{-5n - 4}{(n + 3)(n + 1)}$

34. $\frac{-a^2 - 5a - 3}{(a + 5)(a - 5)}$

35. $\frac{-17t + 27}{(t + 3)(10t - 9)}$

36. $\frac{y^2 + 7y + 6}{(y + 4)(y + 3)}$

37. $\frac{v^2 + 11v - 2}{(v + 4)(v - 1)}$

38. $\frac{2(2a + 5)}{(a - 2)(a + 1)}$, $\frac{-2(2a + 5)}{(a - 2)(a + 1)}$; They are opposite.

39a. 360; 3; 120; 360

39b. 540; 6; 90; 540

39c. The GCF times the LCM of two numbers is equal to the product of the two numbers.

40. 42

39d. Divide the GCF into the product of the two numbers to find the LCM.

41. 15 months later or July 20, 1997

42. 66 years

43. 2

44. $\dfrac{x+6}{3x-2}; -1, \dfrac{2}{3}$

45. $\dfrac{3 \pm \sqrt{41}}{4}$ or about 2.35 and -0.85

46. $3y(x^2 + 2x + 3y)$

47. $-15a^6b^3$

48.

$-6\ -5\ -4\ -3\ -2\ -1\ 0\ 1\ 2\ 3\ 4$

49. 4

50.

Stem	Leaf
0	3
1	0 3 8 9
2	0 0 1 2
3	9
4	5 7 9

$0\,|\,3 = 30$ *thousand*

12–7 Mixed Expressions and Complex Fractions
Pages 693–695

1. $\dfrac{3}{4}$

2a. $2x(x - 2)$

2b. $\dfrac{3x^3 + 10x^2 + 26x - 16}{2x(x - 2)}$

3. $\dfrac{8x + 3}{x}$

4. $\dfrac{15m + 8}{3m}$

5. $\dfrac{6m^2 + m + 1}{2m}$

6. $\dfrac{7}{9}$

7. $\dfrac{9}{5}$

8. $\dfrac{9}{x^2}$

9. $\dfrac{y}{2}$

10. $\dfrac{x + 4}{x + 5}$

11. $\dfrac{a - b}{3}$

12. Division; $\dfrac{x + 2}{3x - 1} \div \dfrac{2x^2 - 8}{3x - 1} =$

$\dfrac{x + 2}{3x - 1} \cdot \dfrac{3x - 1}{2(x - 2)(x + 2)} = \dfrac{1}{2(x - 2)}$

13. $\dfrac{3x + 15}{x + 3}$

14. $\dfrac{12a + 10b}{a + b}$

15. $\dfrac{6x - 1}{2x + 1}$

16. $\dfrac{4x + 3y - 4}{x + y}$

17. $\dfrac{5r^2 + r - 48}{r^2 - 9}$

18. $\dfrac{4x^2 - 2y^2}{x^2 - y^2}$

19. $\dfrac{4}{3}$

20. $\dfrac{5}{7}$

21. ab

22. a^2y

23. $\dfrac{6}{x}$

24. $\dfrac{8}{y}$

Algebra 1

25. $\dfrac{a-5}{a-2}$

26. $\dfrac{x+5}{x+12}$

27. $\dfrac{1}{x+3}$

28. $\dfrac{m+7}{m+5}$

29. $\dfrac{m+6}{m+2}$

30. $\dfrac{(a+4)(a-1)(a+2)}{(a+5)(a^2+2)}$

31. $\dfrac{y-3}{y+2}$

32. $\dfrac{(x+2)(x-1)(x+3)}{(x-2)(x^2+2x-5)}$

33. $\dfrac{t^2+2t+2}{-t^2}$

34. $\dfrac{a(b^2+1)}{b(a^2+1)}$

35. $\dfrac{32b^2}{35}$

36. $\dfrac{5x+3}{3x+2}$

37a. $x \neq 0,$
$x \neq -3$

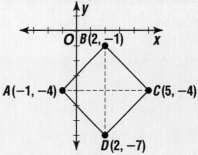

38. 6

37b. $x \neq 0,\ x \neq -3$

37c. yes

39a. $\dfrac{fs}{s-v}$

40. approximately 1061

39b. 413.5

39c. 2

39d. 6

41. $\dfrac{2x+3}{x+3}$

42. $\dfrac{1}{3}$

43. $(2x+1)(2x-1)$

44. x^3y^2

45. $(-3,-4)$

46a. Opposite sides are parallel, adjacent sides are perpendicular, perpendicular diagonals.

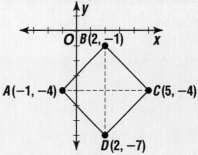

46b. square

47. $w = \dfrac{P-2\ell}{2}$

48. 15

12–8 Solving Rational Equations
Pages 699–702

1. 2 hours

2. She correctly solved the equation, but $m = 1$ makes a denominator zero and it must therefore be discarded as a solution.

3. A rational equation contains rational expressions whereas a linear equation has integer coefficients.

4a–b. See students' work.

5. -12

6. $-\dfrac{5}{2}$

7. $-\dfrac{1}{2}$

8. $-3, 2$

9. 0

10. 3

11a. $\dfrac{1}{5}$

11b. $\dfrac{3}{5}$

11c. $\dfrac{x}{5}$

12.

	d	r	$t = \dfrac{d}{r}$
downstream	9	$3 + c$	$\dfrac{9}{3 + c}$
upstream	3	$3 - c$	$\dfrac{9}{3 - c}$

12a. $\dfrac{9}{3 + c} = \dfrac{3}{3 - c}$

12b. 1.5 mph

13. 3.429 ohms

14. 4 ohms

15. 8 ohms, 4 ohms

16. -8

17. $\dfrac{50}{3}$

18. $x = -1$ or $x = -2$

19. $\dfrac{5}{4}$

20. $\dfrac{-3}{2}$

21. 0

22. 1 or -3

23. 2 or $-\dfrac{1}{3}$

24. -6 or $-\dfrac{2}{3}$

25. 4 or $-\dfrac{1}{3}$

26. 3

27. -13

28. 8

29. $\dfrac{3}{5}$

30. $\dfrac{3}{25}$

31. 3

32. 3, 1

33. 6

34. 2.92 ohms

35. 4 ohms

36. $7.\overline{6}$ ohms

Algebra 1

37. $R_1 = \dfrac{R_2 R_T}{R_2 - R_T}$

38. $R = \dfrac{E - Ir}{I}$

39. $n = \dfrac{IR}{E - Ir}$

40. $r = \dfrac{En - IRn}{I}$

41. 10

42a. $R_T = R_1 + \dfrac{R_2 R_3}{R_2 + R_3}$

42b. 7.4 ohms

43. 96 ohms

44. 12.63 ohms

45a. 2.5 hours

46a. $\dfrac{2}{3}$ h or 40 min, $10\dfrac{2}{3}$ miles from one end or $13\dfrac{1}{3}$ miles from the other

45b. 2.19 hours

45c. after 923 miles

46b. 2 mph

46c. 6 hours

47a. $w = \dfrac{\ell c}{100}$

48a. $m = \dfrac{ic}{100}$

47b. $\ell = \dfrac{100w}{c}$

48b. $c = \dfrac{100m}{i}$

49. 10

50. $\dfrac{x + 3}{x + 2}$

51. $\dfrac{b + 4}{4(b + 2)^2}$

52. $0.25a^2 + 0.25ab + 0.0625b^2$

53.
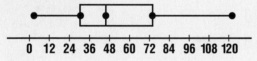

54. 120.31, 45.90, 74.47, 30.67, 43.80; no outliers

55. $\dfrac{48}{25}$

56. -5

57. 18

58. $3x$

Chapter 13 Exploring Radical Expressions and Equations
13–1 Integration: Geometry The Pythagorean Theorem
Pages 715–718

1.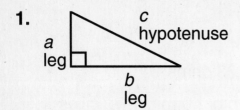

3a. 3, 4, 5

3b. $3^2 + 4^2 \stackrel{?}{=} 5^2$

$9 + 16 \stackrel{?}{=} 25$

$25 = 25$ ✓

5. $16 + 4 = 20$

7. 7

9. 11.40

11. 15

13. 2

15. yes

17. 127.28 ft

19. 13.86

21. 13.08

23. 14.70

25. 60

27. 4

29. $\sqrt{67} \approx 8.19$

31. $\sqrt{27} \approx 5.20$

33. $\sqrt{145} \approx 12.04$

35. yes

37. no; $11^2 + 12^2 \neq 15^2$

39. yes

41. $\sqrt{75}$ in. or about 8.66 in.

43a. 44.49 m

43b. 78 m²

2. By squaring the two shorter sides and adding them; then, comparing their sum to the square of the third, or longer, side. If they are equal, it is a right triangle.

4. Since the Pythagorean theorem finds the length of a side, it has to be positive. Distance is not negative.

6. 13

8. 12

10. 14.14

12. 5

14. $\sqrt{65} \approx 8.06$

16. no; $2^2 + 8^2 \neq 8^2$

18. 8.25

20. 15.20

22. 12.53

24. 34

26. 8

28. $\sqrt{45} \approx 6.71$

30. $\sqrt{21} \approx 4.58$

32. $\sqrt{253} \approx 15.91$

34. no; $6^2 + 9^2 \neq 12^2$

36. yes

38. no; $16^2 + (\sqrt{32})^2 \neq 20^2$

40. 16 cm

42a. $x^2 + (x + 6)^2 = (30)^2$

42b. 18 cm, 24 cm

44a. 7.28

44b. 15

44c. 19.85

44d. 10.82

44e. 20

46. about 116.62 ft

45.

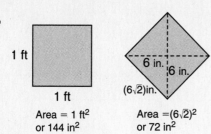

Area = 1 ft² or 144 in²   Area =(6√2)² or 72 in²

47. about 2.66 m

49. −7

48. about 25.5 ft

50. $x = 3$; $(3, -1)$

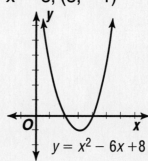

$y = x^2 - 6x + 8$

51. $12r^7$

53. $\left\{c \middle| c \geq \frac{1}{2}\right\}$

55. 41

52. 16, 22

54. −2, 3, $y = -2x + 3$

56. −18

13–2 Simplifying Radical Expressions
Pages 723–725

1. to ensure nonnegative results

2. Multiply the numerator and denominator of a fraction by the same number so that a radical is not left in the denominator.

3. Melanie is correct. In step 4, the square root of a negative number was taken. This value is not defined in the set of real numbers.

4. Sample answer: You may have to take steps so that the radicand contains no perfect squares or fractions.

5. $5 - \sqrt{2}$; 23

6. $\sqrt{3} + \sqrt{7}$; −4

7. $\dfrac{\sqrt{7}}{\sqrt{7}}$

8. $\dfrac{4 + \sqrt{3}}{4 + \sqrt{3}}$

9. $3\sqrt{2}$

10. 2

11. $\dfrac{\sqrt{21}}{7}$

12. $\dfrac{\sqrt{15}}{3}$

13. $10\sqrt{2} + 26$

14. $y^2 - 5$

15. $\dfrac{18 + 6\sqrt{2}}{7}$

16. $4\,|\,a\,|\,b\sqrt{5b}$

17. $>$

18. $=$

19. about 7003.5 gal/min

20. $5\sqrt{3}$

21. $4\sqrt{5}$

22. $2\sqrt{70}$

23. $10\sqrt{5}$

24. $\dfrac{\sqrt{21}}{3}$

25. $\dfrac{\sqrt{2}}{2}$

26. $\dfrac{\sqrt{14}}{7}$

27. $\dfrac{\sqrt{22}}{8}$

28. 150

29. $84\sqrt{5}$

30. $\dfrac{\sqrt{35}}{5}$

31. $\dfrac{\sqrt{11}}{11}$

32. $2b^2\sqrt{10}$

33. $3\,|\,ab\,|\,\sqrt{6}$

34. $2\,|\,m\,|\,y^2\sqrt{15}$

35. $7x^2y^3\sqrt{3xy}$

36. $\dfrac{\sqrt{2t}}{4}$

37. $\dfrac{3\sqrt{3}}{|\,p\,|}$

38. $\dfrac{n^2\sqrt{5mn}}{2\,|\,m^3\,|}$

39. $\dfrac{x\sqrt{3xy}}{2y^3}$

40. $21 + 4\sqrt{5}$

41. $y^2 - 2y\sqrt{7} + 7$

42. $m + 4\sqrt{5m} + 20$

43. $\dfrac{28\sqrt{2} + 14\sqrt{5}}{3}$

44. $\dfrac{54a - 9a\sqrt{a}}{36 - a}$

45. $\dfrac{-2\sqrt{5} - \sqrt{10}}{2}$

46. $\dfrac{5\sqrt{21} - 3\sqrt{35}}{10}$

47. $\dfrac{c - 2\sqrt{cd} + d}{c - d}$

48. $2x - 6$

49. $x^2 - 5x\sqrt{3} + 12$

50. $=$

51. $>$

52. $>$

53. $<$

54. No, because square roots of negative numbers are not defined in the set of real numbers; $\sqrt{(-2) \cdot (-3)} \neq \sqrt{-2} \cdot \sqrt{-3}$.

55. Yes, the result is about 11.84

56. about 90.83 volts

Algebra 1

57. 18.44 cm

58. $\dfrac{2a-1}{a-8}$; $a \neq 8, -6$

59. $1, \dfrac{2}{3}$

60. $4ab^2(3ab - 7c^2)$

61. 2.7×10^9 acres

62. $\{t \mid t > -6\}$

63. $y = \dfrac{1}{5}x + 6$

64. $\{(-1, 3), (-1, 4), (1, 4), (1, -3), (3, 5)\}$; D = $\{-1, 1, 3)$; R = $\{3, 4, -3, 5\}$

65. -6

67. $\dfrac{1}{4}x^2$

13–3 Operations with Radical Expressions
Pages 729–731

1. Sample answer: $4\sqrt{3}, 2\sqrt{3}, 6\sqrt{3}$

2. to determine if there are any like radicands

3. Sample answer:
$\sqrt{x} + \sqrt{y} \overset{?}{=} \sqrt{x+y}$
$\sqrt{3} + \sqrt{6} \overset{?}{=} \sqrt{9}$
$4.1815 \neq 3$

4. The distributive property allows you to add like terms. Radicals with like radicands can be added or subtracted.

5. $3\sqrt{5}, 3\sqrt{20}$

6. $-5\sqrt{7}, 2\sqrt{28}$

7. none

8. $9\sqrt{32}, 2\sqrt{50}, 3\sqrt{200}$

9. $13\sqrt{6}$

10. in simplest form

11. $12\sqrt{7x}$

12. $11\sqrt{5}$; 24.60

13. $13\sqrt{3} + \sqrt{2}$; 23.93

14. $4\sqrt{3}$; 6.93

15. $\dfrac{8}{7}\sqrt{7}$; 3.02

16. $6 + 4\sqrt{6}$

17. 11

18. $8\sqrt{7} - 6\sqrt{3}$; $4\sqrt{21} - 12$

19. $26\sqrt{13}$

20. 0

21. in simplest form

22. $-7\sqrt{11}$

23. $21\sqrt{2x}$

24. $-2\sqrt{5m}$

25. $9\sqrt{3}$; 15.59

26. $-10\sqrt{5}$; -22.36

27. $\sqrt{6} + 2\sqrt{2} + \sqrt{10}$; 8.44

28. $4\sqrt{6} - 6\sqrt{2} + 5\sqrt{7}$; 14.54

29. $-\sqrt{7}$; -2.65

30. $-2\sqrt{2}$; -2.83

31. $29\sqrt{3}$; 50.23

32. $-2\sqrt{5} - 6\sqrt{6}$; -19.17

33. $4\sqrt{5} + 15\sqrt{2}$; 30.16

34. $\dfrac{4}{5}\sqrt{10}$; 2.53

35. $4\sqrt{3} - 3\sqrt{5}$; 0.22

36. $\dfrac{53\sqrt{7}}{7}$; 20.03

37. $10\sqrt{2} + 3\sqrt{10}$

38. $3\sqrt{2} + 10\sqrt{3}$

39. $19\sqrt{5}$

40. $3\sqrt{7}$

41. $10\sqrt{3} + 16$

42. $15\sqrt{2} + 11\sqrt{5}$

43. Both $(x - 5)^2$ and $(x - 5)^4$ must be nonnegative, but $x - 5$ may be negative.

44. $\sqrt{1005} - \sqrt{795}$; 3.51 mi

45. $6\frac{2}{5}$ ft

46. $\frac{\sqrt{2}}{2}$

47. $3x - 3y$

48. $(3a - 2)(a + 7)$

49. 7

50. 45

51. $\frac{2}{3}$

52. $21°$

53a. 1991; about 9 million

53b. 6 million

Self Test
Page 731

1. 35

2. 4.80

3. 46.17

4. $2\sqrt{5}$

5. 10

6. $\dfrac{|x|\sqrt{7y}}{y^2}$

7. $11\sqrt{6}$

8. $2\sqrt{17} + 15\sqrt{7}$

9. $12\sqrt{5} - 6\sqrt{3} + 2\sqrt{15} - 3$

10. 53.37 cm, 138 cm²

13–4 Radical Equations
Pages 734–736

1. Isolate the radical.

2. $\pm\sqrt{7y}$

3a. $d = \left(\dfrac{s}{3.1}\right)^2$

4. Ellen is correct; for $\sqrt{x} = -4$, there is no real solution.

3b. about 16,649 m

5a. Sample answer: Isolate the radical, square both sides of the equation, and simplify.

6. $x = 36$

5b. The solution may not satisfy the original equation.

7. $a + 3 = 4$

8. $169 = 2y - 5$

9. 16

10. no real solution

11. 36

12. 7

13. −12

14. 66

15. 3.9 mph

16. 60

17. −63

18. 16

19. no real solution

20. 27

21. $\dfrac{81}{25}$

22. 3

23. 2

24. no real solution

25. 24

26. 180

27. $\dfrac{3}{25}$

28. 11

29. $\pm\dfrac{4}{3}\sqrt{3}$

30. 7

31. $\sqrt{7}$

32. 0

33. 6

34. 96

35. −3, −10, or 3, 10

36. $-\dfrac{16}{3}$, −27 or 9, 16

37. 16

38. 0

39. no real solution

40. (9, 0)

41. $\left(\dfrac{1}{4}, \dfrac{25}{36}\right)$

42. (16, 4)

43. $\sqrt{3} + 1$

44. 16 and 9

45. $54\dfrac{2}{3}$ mi

46a. 43.84°C

46b. 16°C

47a. No, at 30 mph her car should have skidded 75 feet after the brakes were applied and not 110 feet.

48. $-3\sqrt{6} - 8\sqrt{3}$

47b. about 36 miles per hour

49. $6b - 26 + \dfrac{150}{b + 5}$

50. −2, 4

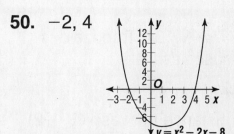

51. $6xy^2$

52. $2a - 9m$

53. (−4, 5)

54. $y = -x + 5$

55. $\dfrac{8}{13}$

56. $-\dfrac{1}{63}$

13–5 Integration: Geometry   The Distance Formula
Pages 738–741

1. The values that are subtracted are squared before being added, the square of a negative is always positive, and distances are never negative numbers.

2a–b. See students' work.

3a. The distance between them is the absolute value of the difference of their x-coordinates, $|12 - 3|$ or 9 units.

4. See students' work.

3b. The distance between them is the absolute value of the difference of their y-coordinates, $|7 - (-5)|$ or 12 units.

5. 5

6. 13

7. $3\sqrt{2}$ or 4.24

8. $\sqrt{185}$ or 13.60

9. 7 or 1

10. -2 or 4

11. about 9.49 mi

12. 10

13. 17

14. $4\sqrt{5}$ or 8.94

15. $\sqrt{41}$ or 6.40

16. $2\sqrt{13}$ or 7.21

17. $\frac{10}{3}$ or 3.33

18. $\frac{\sqrt{74}}{7}$ or 1.23

19. $\frac{13}{10}$ or 1.30

20. $2\sqrt{14}$ or 7.48

21. $2\sqrt{3}$ or 3.46

22. 9 or -3

23. 17 or -13

24. -2 or -12

25. -10 or 4

26. 2 or -14

27. 8 or 32

28. yes

29. no

30. $12\sqrt{10}$ or 37.9 units

31. $\sqrt{157} \neq \sqrt{101}$; Trapezoid is not isosceles.

32a. 10

32b. ≈16.55

32c. ≈13.88

33. The distance between $(3, -2)$ and $(-3, 7)$ is $3\sqrt{13}$ units. The distance between $(-3, 7)$ and $(-9, 3)$ is $2\sqrt{13}$ units. The distance between $(3, -2)$ and

34. 18 in.

(−9, 3) is 13 units. Since $(3\sqrt{13})^2 + (2\sqrt{13})^2 = 13^2$, the triangle is a right triangle.

35. 109 miles

37. $\dfrac{2\sqrt{2}}{3}$

39. No solution

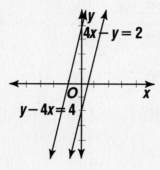

36. 4 seconds

38. $4p$

40. $43.50

41a. 7392 BTU

41b. 3705 BTU

41c. 6247.5 BTU

41d. 14,040 BTU

41e. 6831.45 BTU

13–6 Solving Quadratic Equations by Completing the Square
Pages 745–747

1. completing the square

2. Step 1: Find one-half of b.
Step 2: Square the result of Step 1.
Step 3: Add the result of Step 2 to $x^2 + bx$.

3. Sample answer: $x^2 + 4x + 12 = 0$, $(x + 2)^2 = -8$; Since the number of the right side is negative, there are no real roots.

4. $(x + 3)^2 = 7$

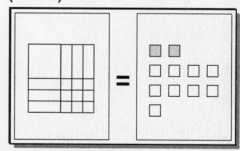

$$x^2 + 6x + 9 = -2 + 9$$
$$(x + 3)^2 = 7$$

5. 64

6. $\dfrac{49}{4}$

7. −1, −3

8. 1, 7

9. 7, −3

10. $\dfrac{5}{2}$

11. $2 \pm \sqrt{6}$

12. $\dfrac{5}{2}$, −4

13. 4.9 ft

14. 9

15. 16

16. $\dfrac{25}{4}$

17. $\dfrac{121}{4}$

18. 9

19. 8

20. −3, −4

21. 4, 1

22. 1, −15

23. $\dfrac{7}{3}$

24. $12 \pm 3\sqrt{15}$

25. $3 \pm \sqrt{5}$

26. $4 \pm 2\sqrt{5}$

27. $5 \pm 4\sqrt{3}$

28. $3, \dfrac{1}{2}$

29. $\dfrac{-5 \pm 2\sqrt{15}}{5}$

30. $-\dfrac{3}{2}, 4$

31. $\dfrac{2}{3}, -1$

32. $-0.125 \pm \sqrt{0.515625}$

33. $\dfrac{7 \pm \sqrt{85}}{6}$

34. $\dfrac{5 \pm \sqrt{17}}{4}$

35. 18, −18

36. 60, −60

37. 3

38. $\dfrac{9}{4}$

39. $2 \pm \sqrt{4 - c}$

40. $\dfrac{-b \pm \sqrt{b^2 - 4c}}{2}$

41. $b(-2 \pm \sqrt{3})$

42a. $y = (x - 4)^2 - 1$

42b.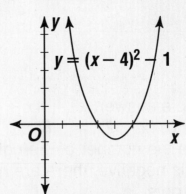

$y = (x - 4)^2 - 1$

42c. It is the vertex of the graph.

43. 45 mph, 55 mph

44a. $(15 + 2x)(10 + 2x) = 1800$; 15 ft

44b. 45 ft by 40 ft

45. 8.06

46. no

47. 2042

48. $5y^2 + 7y - 6$

49. (2, 2)

50a. IV

50b. II

50c. III

51a. 224.6

52. 27

51b. 172